KU-303-928

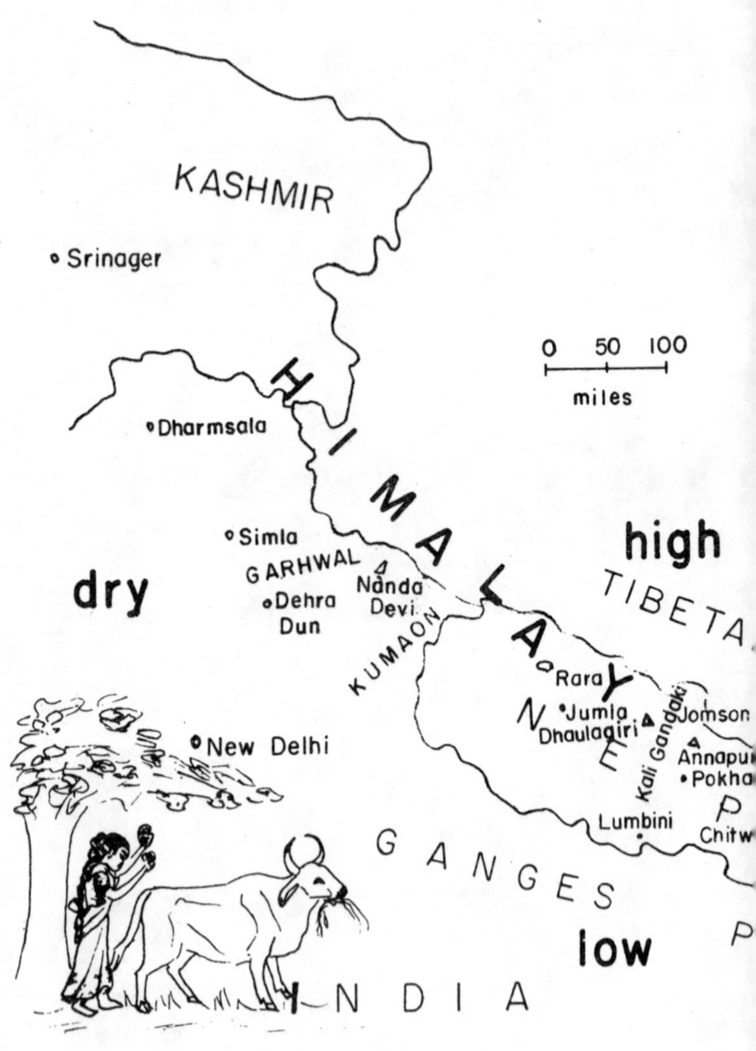

KASHMIR
Srinager
0 50 100
miles
Dharmsala
HIMALAY
Simla
high
TIBETA
GARHWAL
Nanda
Devi
dry
Dehra
Dun
KUMAON
Rara
Jumla
Dhaulagiri
Kali Gandaki
Jomson
NEP
New Delhi
Annapu
Pokha
Lumbini
Chitw
GANGES P
low
INDIA

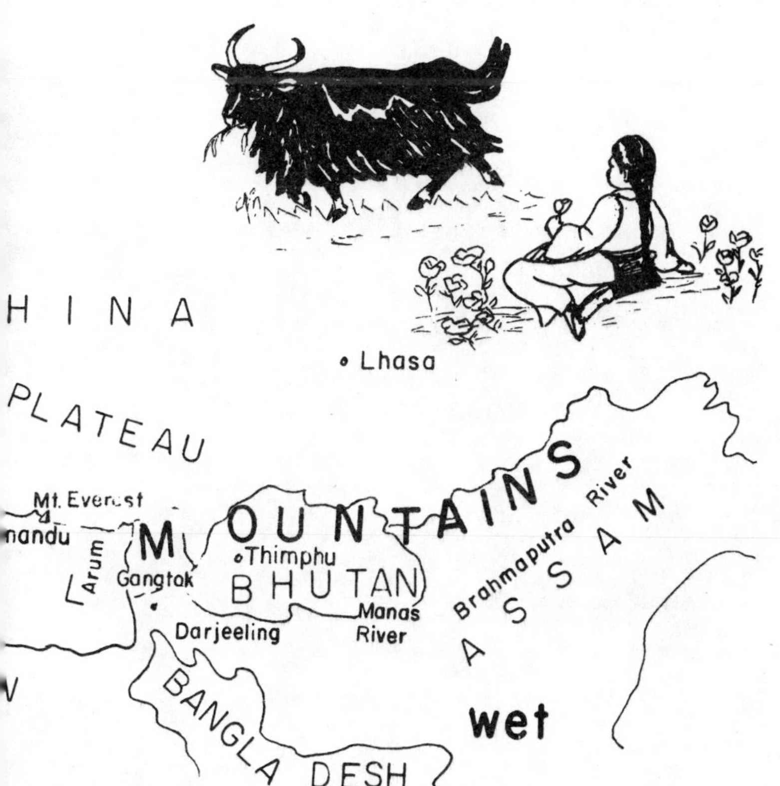
H I N A
Lhasa
PLATEAU
Mt. Everest
nandu
Arum
MOUNTAINS
Thimphu
Gangtok
BHUTAN
Brahmaputra River
ASSAM
Manas River
Darjeeling
BANGLA DESH
wet

HIMALAYAN FLOWERS AND TREES

DOROTHY MIEROW
TIRTHA BAHADUR SHRESTHA

SAHAYOGI PRESS
Tripureshwar, Kathmandu, Nepal

Published by
Sahayogi Prakashan
Tripureshwar, Kathmandu, Nepal
Telephone: 11489
First Printing September 1978
Second Printing May 1987

SAHAYOGI PRAKASHAN
Tripureshwar, Kathmandu, Nepal

Cover pictures; front; *Rhododendron arboreum,* Nepalese National Flower

back; "Chautara" or resting place by tree near Ampipal and Tibetan child with goat in Pokhara with Annapurna range.

On title page: Wild Pea flowers *Lathyrus*

Printed by Craftsman Press Ltd. Thailand

TABLE OF CONTENTS

INTRODUCTION

The highest mountain range in the world separates the two most populated countries of the world, India and China. It has served both as a barrier and haven of retreat to the peoples of the region. Many different tribes and ethnic groups kept or developed different languages and customs. The variety of climate found at different altitudes and exposures of the mountains has made it necessary for people to live in many different ways. Tibetan type people build flat-roofed houses and dress warmly to protect themselves against the cold winds in their dry valleys and plateaus north and west of the Great Himalayas. Nepalis from Garhwal through Bhutan have terraced the middle slopes for agriculture and built houses of local materials in styles suitable to their various ways of life.

Until recently, the foothills remained forested as they harbored the deadly malaria mosquito. Only a few Tharu people could resist the sickness, so a belt of natural jungle separated the hill people from the people of the Ganges plain.

In the monsoon tropics of the plains and lower foothills it becomes cool in the dry winter but does not freeze Here it is the heavy summer rains which are most important as they bring green plants and crops as well as serious erosion problems and floods. Houses may be of simple mud, grass, leaves and sticks or they may be raised from the ground on platforms away from the dampness and made of wood or cement. Local conditions and traditions vary but not as much as in the hills and mountains.

It is the same with the trees and flowers of the Himalayas. They too have to adapt in order to survive in the many different conditions of climate, soil and topography found in the Himalayas.

The high plateaus and dry valleys are treeless. Alpine plants are often covered with hairs which protect them from evaporation or water loss due to strong winds. The growing season is short and plants are scattered and growing close to the ground. The species are often related to those found in the mountains of temperate Europe, Asia and North America. The sparcely scattered desert vegetation is also often prickly or succulent with tiny leaves. Many species are the same as those found in the Mediterranean countries and desert country of the Middle East.

Isolated valleys may often harbor distinctive species or varieties of plants when the mountains have cut off contact with the mother species.

This is very different from the tropical plains near sea level. There, the year-round conditions for plant growth are excellent in terms of temperature and moisture. Even in the wet-dry monsoon region, tall trees and vines struggle for the sunlight and crowd out most of the smaller herbaceous plants. In legendary and early historical times the Ganges Plain was a vast forest— a retreat for the Ascetic and the setting for many a Princely hunt. Today it is the rice bowl and often dispair of India as cropland has replaced the forests.

Today the slopes of the Himalayas are still forested between about 7,600 ft. and the upper treeline at around 13,000 ft. except in the rainshadow valleys or where they have been burned to provide more grass for grazing. Conifers ascend to a natural timberline of 12,000 or 14,000 ft. at this relatively low latitude. These evergreen and the temperate broadleaf trees and associated flowers found mixed with them or slightly lower are often familiar to residents of temperate Europe, Asia and North America.

As one moves down into the Subtropics, new species more familiar to the people of the Indian sub-continent begin to appear. The longer growing season with a period of drought between the melting of winter snow higher up and monsoon rains coming from the Bay of Bengal has made this elevation subject to man-made fires. Only resistant vegetation may survive in those areas where grass for grazing is desired more than natural forests, and terraced farmland is needed by the ever growing population.

This is a man-made region. The needs of the moment have too often overshadowed the needs for the future. Firewood becomes more expensive as it becomes scarcer. Native forests are disappearing or being replaced with sturdy, fast growing foreign trees. Commercial crops are valued more than natural growth as population pressure on the land increases.

In general, the rainfall increases and the forests become more luxuriant as one goes to the east in the Himalayas. More species which are from the region of SE Asia appear and dry region plants decrease in numbers east of the Kali Gandaki river between Dhaulagiri and Annapurna mountains. Bhutan still has virgin forests at this level, protected in the Manas River Sanctuary.

The casual visitor to Kathmandu is sometimes a bit disappointed to discover that most of the largest and most beautiful flowering trees, vines, and flowers were introduced from somewhere else in the world and planted along the streets and in the gardens.

Eucalyptus, Bottlebrush and Silky oak came from Australia. The tall, stiff Monkey puzzle tree came from South America as did the Bougainvillea and Poincettia which is famous in Pokhara. The lovely blue Wisteria is a native of China and most of the garden flowers were introduced from Europe, Africa or the Middle East. The marigold, used for religious *pujas,* grows like a native throughout Nepal but had its origin in eastern Europe.

Even many of the crops which are accepted as common local food had their origins elsewhere. Tomatoes, potatoes, red peppers and probably maize came from the Americas and many vegetables now found in the market had a European origin.

Gardens of exotic tiees, flowers and vegetables were planted and spread wherever Gurkha recruiting and Pension paying posts were established by the British. The Rana rulers planted beautiful gardens and also planted shade trees, not only along streets in Kathmandu but also in main Government centres. Citizens as well as rulers have been responsible for planting shade trees on resting platforms along the trails for the traveler. These trees on Chautaras are often members of the Fig Family and planted in pairs, like the Banyan and the Peepul. Many other species may be found, but these two have a religious significance and are often very large and beautiful, especially closer to India where they are native. Many hilltops have temples surrounded by beautiful trees, often with religious significance. The temples and resting places have usually been built by someone to indicate their religious devotion and to honor a family member who has died. A small stone is often placed between the trees and inscribed by the donor.

But where are the natives? A flight over the Midlands of Nepal will reveal the vast regions of terraced hills. The fresh green of the rice paddies or young wheat makes a charming scene which is complimented in many places by the darker green of forests higher up or on the steeper slopes. Too often, however, a closer look reveals that the forests are overcut and are now only low tangled scrub growth. Other hills are bare, cut with gulleys where former streams once flowed through woods. Monsoon rains have eroded the good soil away after woodcutters and graizing animals have taken more than their share.

Not all landslides and erosion in the Himalayas can be blamed on human activities of cutting, burning and overgrazing. Since the mountains are geologically young and still rising, there are many steep slopes with loosely consolidated rocks and soil. Heavy monsoon rains and numerous small earthquakes may start slides even in forested areas. Cutting and overgrazing increase the chances of landslides and soil loss in this fragil situation.

Population pressure is observed even in the most isolated mountains. The virgin forests between Jumla and Rara Lake and the remaining forests of the upper Arun Valley and other places are slowly being cut away by banding and fire to make way for fields which will produce millet or maize two or three years before losing their fertility and being abandoned. The natives are crying for protection.

All love flowers but not everyone is able to grow them. Wild flowers belong to everyone but we are also all responsible for their protection. When people are forced to destroy all of the woods near their homes for the sake of firewood, they are cutting off the branch upon which they sit. Reverence for life and concern for future generations is needed.

Nepal, India, and Bhutan are establishing National Parks to protect what is left before it is too late. The success of these projects concerns all the people of the world.

Actually the number of species native to the Himalayan Region staggers the imagination. Many of the most loved garden plants of the western world had their origin in this region :— Rhododendrons, Magnolias, Spirea, Barberry, Deodar Cedar and many Primroses and Mountain Poppies to mention but a few. It would be impossible to picture all native species in a book of this size.

The best way to see flowers is to walk and in Nepal trekking has become increasingly popular. The pictures of flowers are arranged mainly according to regions where they were taken. This does not necessarily mean that they are limited to the region but if a trek is taken to that region in a comparable season, one is likely to find these flowers. Under similar conditions, they or related species may be seen in other parts of the Himalayas. Thus we find the ecological grouping of some of the flowers of the dry region of the far west, somewhat similar to those found north of Pokhara in Thakkhola. Since it is also interesting to keep members of the same flower family together, related flowers are often shown together even though they may not be found together.

Around Gorkha and Chitwan are found the more tropical forms which we meet again in Eastern Nepal as the Arun Valley near Tumlingtar airport is barely 1,700 ft. above sea level.

The season is naturally important in considering which flowers will be seen. The best time to see Rhododendrons is March and April and from eastern Nepal to Bhutan there are many more species to be seen than west of the Arun Valley. If one treks from Solu to Khumbu in late March or April the Magnolia trees will be in full bloom. Fall in the Everest area or Langtang Valley is the season to see Gentians and Edelweiss. Summer monsoon season is not generally considered a good time to trek but this is the time for Alpine flowers and the Gosainkund region north of Kathmandu is a veritable flower garden. Mushrooms are abundant then in the forests of Helumbu. Primulas gladden the heart at almost every season but are especially abundant in the spring when the Daphne and Rhododendron also bloom. The great red blooms of the Simal tree start appearing as early as January and they are followed by the red blooms of the Phaledo trees. In October and early November when most plants have finished blooming the pink Luculia blossoms brighten the cliff sides from 3,000 ft. up to 6 000 ft. and the little yellow Sunshine flower cheers the trails in January.

Good trails have made good trekking and the very people whose need for firewood and grazing land have destroyed much of the virgin forest have made it possible for all of us to get into the mountains to enjoy the beauty of the mountain flowers.

CHARACTERISTICS OF SOME PLANT FAMILIES FOUND IN NEPAL

Although it would be difficult to learn the names of all species of flowers found in the Himalayas, it is possible to identify many otherwise unknown flowers according to their families. Characteristics of plant families include the number and arrangement of petals, sepals, stamens and the ovary or type of seeds. Sometimes leaf types and arrangement with stem characteristics, growth habits or some unique character is sufficient to recognize the member of a family without seeing the flower. Floral diagrams and formulas are sometimes used for a quick shorthand guide. Only the most obvious distinguishing characters will be used here for quick identification. This is sometimes shown best with a simple sketch.

We generally find more species of woody plants (trees, vines and bushes) in the lower tropics and sub-tropics. Herbaceous plants are most abundant in the higher, more temperate regions. It is the trees and vines that produce the showy flowers in the tropics. Tall grass and thorny undergrowth takes over often when the tropical forest is cut. Clerodendrons, blue Acanthus and white Moonvines stand out as the more showy flowers that are not trees. The Legume or bean family is well represented in trees and vines and even composites approach the size of small trees or grow like vines.

There are so many plant families, especially in the tropics, that it becomes very difficult except in a few fairly well known cases to classify them even into families at a glance. Consequently only those families which can be relatively easily distinguished or which contain numerous well known plants or trees will be discussed. Members of other families may be pictured and the index will list all pictures by families.

MONOCOTYLEDON FAMILIES AT A GLANCE

Classifying and identifying plants is easier if the smaller group of Monocotyledons is separated first. There are only about 40,000 species of Monocotyledons described in the world while 160,000 species of the more diverse Dicotyledons have been described!

Since growth takes place within the stem instead of outer layers being added there are fewer trees and little branching except at the nodes of these plants. The leaves have veins that are parallel rather than branching also.

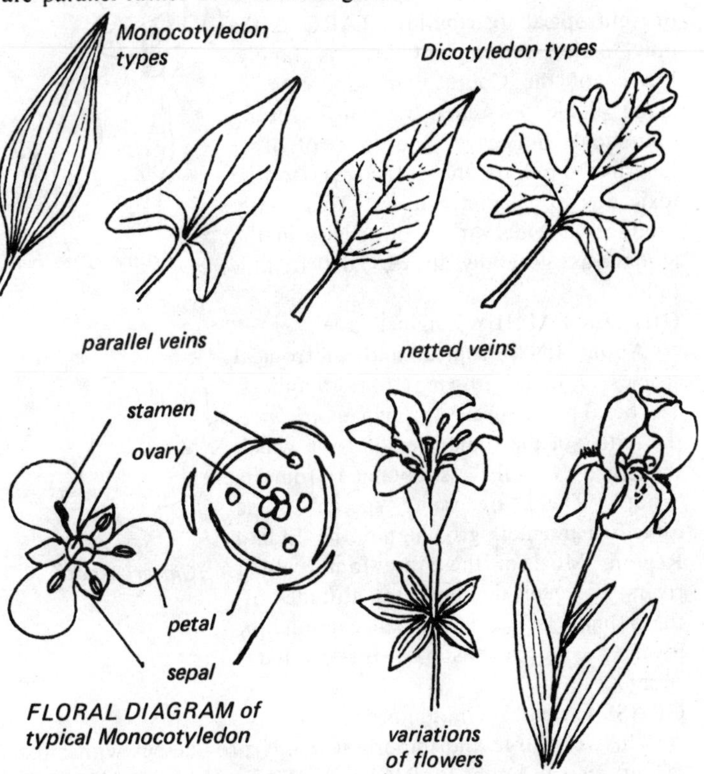

LILY FAMILY Liliaceae

As with other members of the Monocotyledons, the flower parts are in threes or multiples of threes. 3 or 6 petals (sepals look like petals often), 6 stamens and 3 pistils or carpels. This is a very large and important family of about 2,503 species. Food plants in this family include the ONION, CHIVES, ASPARAGUS, and SAFFRON. Many very beautiful garden flowers are members of this family. In Nepal we find some of these large lilies growing wild.

The Iris, Amaryllis, Sisal and Century Plant belong to families closely related to the Lilies.

ARUM FAMILY Araceae

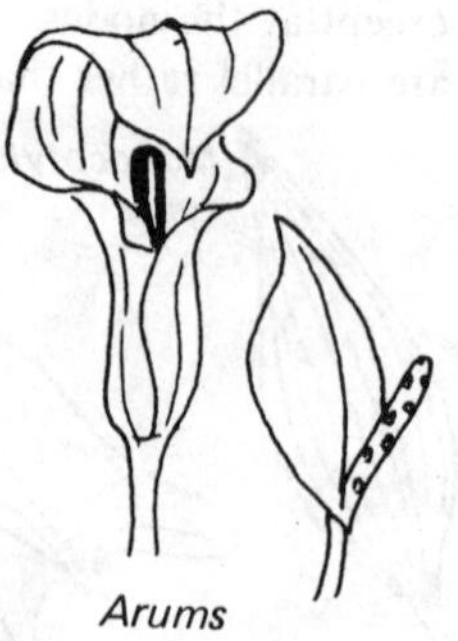
Arums

Contains about 1,500 species of tropical or subtropical distribution. TARO is the only major food plant in this family. Leaves of the Cobra Plant are used to make pickle or Achar by many Gurung households but leaves and roots of other Jack-in-the-pulpits have proved to be toxic due to calcium oxalite. This family produces a wide variety of species in the Himalayas. generally above, 5,000 ft. altitude.

GINGER FAMILY Zingiberaceae

Ginger "Root"

About 1,400 tropical and subtropical species of herbs growing from rhyomesz. The best known species is *Zingiber offlcinale*, the native of the Indian region from which the spice GINGER is obtained from its "root". There are many species, some quite ornamental, growing in the Indian Region. Most of these are found along rivers, especially in the lower altitudes of the Himalayas. Some smaller mountain forms are often mistaken for ground orchids.

GRASS FAMILY Grammineae

This very large and important family provides us with most of our cereal grains – RICE, WHEAT, MAIZE, MILLET, BARLEY plus SUGAR CANE, THATCH, and even BAMBOO. Many wild grasses cover entire areas of the world so that they have been named to indicate this – Alpine meadows, Steppes, Savannahs, short and tall grass Prairies. Fires often favor grasslands in places normally wet enough for forests to grow. Moderate grazing keeps grass in good condition but overgrazing may encourage undesirable weed growth or promote serious erosion problems if the grass roots are destroyed.

ORCHID FAMILY Orchidaceae

The Himalayas are rich in orchids. Both terrestrial and epiphytic forms are found. Most have green leaves and can make their own food material but a few non-green saprophytes have scale leaves and depend upon a fungus for organic food. They do not harm the trees upon which they grow. The 20,000 species of orchids are divided into 800 genera. Many of those found in Nepal can be found on trunks and branches of trees growing in the sub-tropical and temperate regions.

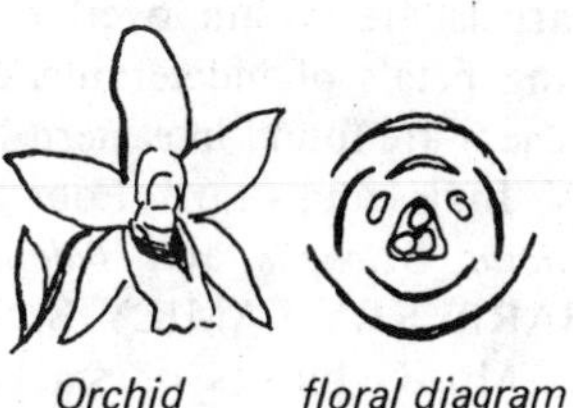
Orchid floral diagram

SEDGES and many WATER PLANTS such as water plantains, rushes, floating pond weeds, and arrowheads are also MONOCOTYLEDONS. They often have Triangular stems.

The only trees in the Monocotyledon Order are BANANAS or PLANTAINS, PALMS, PANDANUS, and BAMBOO.

BROOMRAPE FAMILY Orobanchaceae

Members of this group are often mistaken for terrestrial orchids. They are yellow or colorless parasites on the roots of other plants. The flowers resemble *Scrophulariaceae*

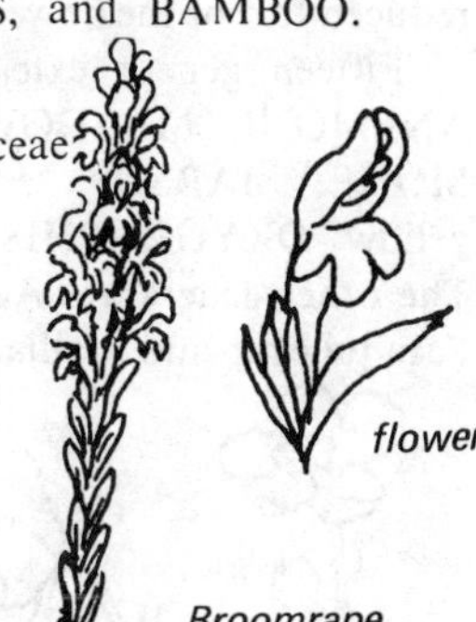
flower

Broomrape

A FEW DICOTYLEDON FAMILIES

MAGNOLIA FAMILY Magnoliaceae

Appears to be one of the most primitive of the flower families. Mostly trees and shrubs, often with large, showy white or pink flowers which may appear before the leaves. Numerous spirally arranged stamens and three

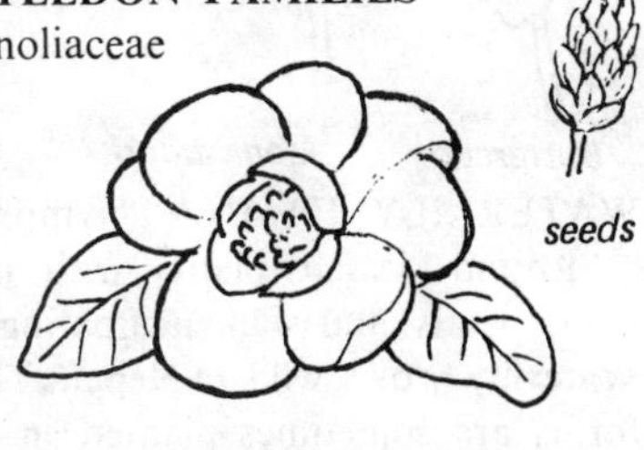
seeds

Magnolia

carpels are within overlapping petals of indeterminate number. About 100 species in 100 genera are found in eastern N. A. and east Asia, Japan, Malaya, W. Indies and Brazil. Four genera are in Nepal *Magnolia, Manglietia, Michelia* and *Talauma.*

BARBERRY FAMILY Berberidaceae

Mostly bushes or small herbs with small thorns at base of leaves and yellow sepals and petals in whorls of 3 to 9. Fruit is a berry. Three genera are found in Nepal : *Berberis, Mahonia* (almost a small tree with bright yellow wood) and *Podophyllum* (May apple).

Barberry

BUTTERCUP FAMILY Ranunculaceae

Found mainly in cooler regions of the Northern Hemisphere or in high altitudes of the Himalayas. The flower structure is similar to that of the Magnolia though the petals are often reduced to 5 or the flowers may be irregular.

Fifteen genera extend into Nepal including CLEMATIS, ANEMONE, MEADOW RUE, BUTTERCUP, WOOD ANEMONE, MARSH MARIGOLD, GLOBE FLOWER, tiny yellow OXYGRAPHIS, LARKSPUR and MONKSHOOD. The other genera are Actaea, Naravelia, Cimicifuga, Aquilegia, Paraquilegia and Callianthemum.

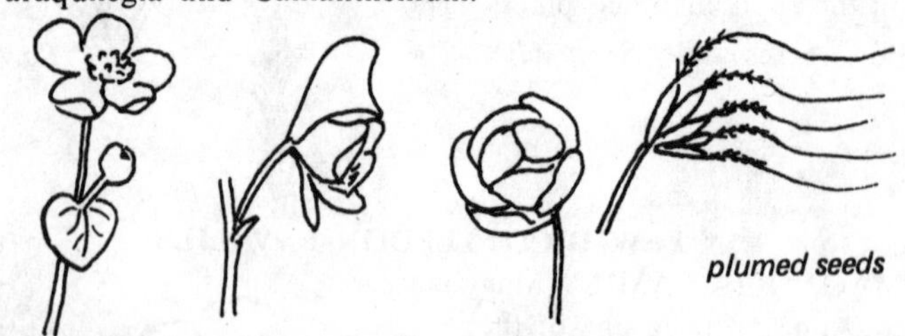

plumed seeds

Buttercup *Monkshood* *Globeflower*

WATERLILY FAMILY Nymphaeceae

Round leafed plants with large showy white flowers of many petals and stamens floating on water. Only the white Waterlily grows wild in Nepal. The Indian Lotus and colored forms are sometimes planted in pools, and were probably introduced from Britain.

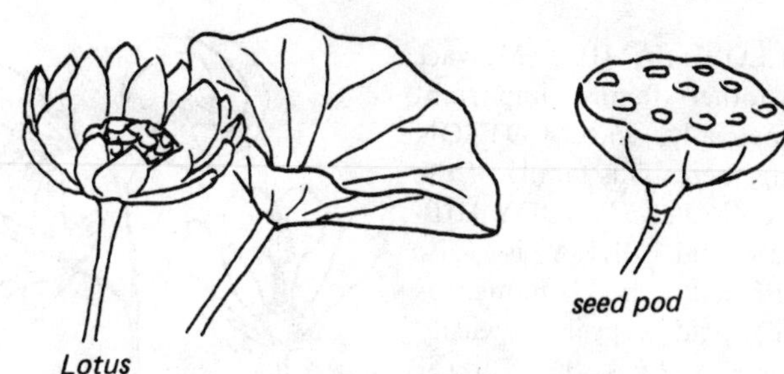

Lotus

POPPY FAMILY Papaveraceae

Stems and other parts contain milky or colored juice (latex).

Flowers generally have 2 sepals (which may fall off as the flower opens) and 4 (often large and crumpled) petals. Many stamens. Seeds contained in capsule and can be shaken out. Four genera are found in Nepal : *Papaver* includes OPIUM POPPY from which we get Morphine and the large yellow or red ORIENTAL POPPIES, *Argemone* with spiny leaves, *Meconopsis* famous for its variety of colors in species– yellow, red white, and even blue and *Stylophorum*.

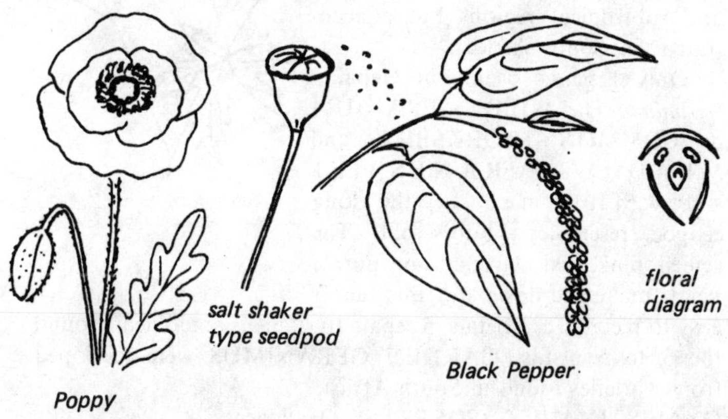

Poppy

Black Pepper

PEPPER FAMILY Piperaceae

BLACK PEPPER and BETEL LEAVES (*P. bettle*) are the best known commercial crops in this large family of over 1,300 species. Most are herbs, shrubs or climbers found in the tropics or sub-tropics. A number of important medicinal plants are in this family.

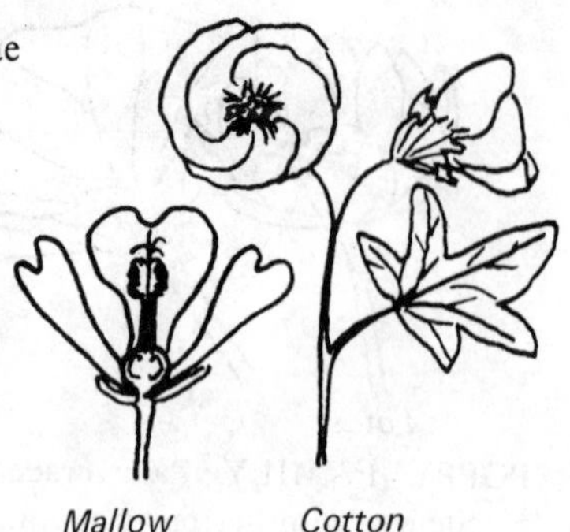
Mallow (section) Cotton

MALLOW FAMILY Malvaceae

Another family important commercially, since COTTON belongs here. This family of the HOLLYHOCK, WOODY HIBISCUS and OKRA is also represented by numerous small wild species easily identified by the flower and the mucilage in the stem and leaves. 5 genera in Nepal: *Malva, Pida, Urema, Hibiscus* & *Thespesia*. A funnel-shaped corolla of 5 petals surround the many stamens on a sheath enveloping the pistils.

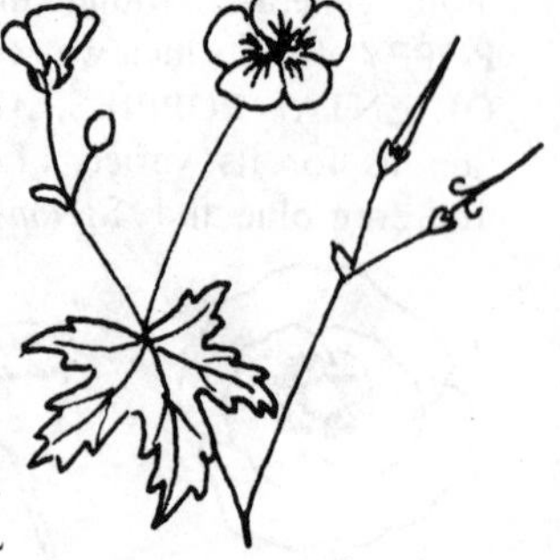
Geranium

GERANIUM FAMILY Geraniaceae

The 700 species of this family are widely distributed in N. temperate and subtropical regions but concentrated in South Africa.

Only 1 genus occurs in Nepal – *Geranium*. The WILD GERANIUM or COMMON STORKSBILL and MEADOW CRANESBILL are well named as the long eedpod resembles a bird's bill. The veined pink, red, lavender or purple petals make the flowers of this family easy to recognize. 5 petals, 5 sepals 10 stamens are joined around the 3 to 5 pistils. GARDEN GERANIMUS were developed from varieties found in South Africa.

OXALIS FAMILY (SORRELS) Oxalidaceae

Herbaceous plants with sour juice. The sensitive clover-like compound leaves and purple or yellow Germanium-like flowers identify most members of this groups. 2 genera are in Nepal: *Oxalis* and *Biophytum*. An evergreen tree (CAROMBOLA) grows in tropical India and produces a juicy acid or sweet fruit. most other members of this family are small.

MUSTARD FAMILY Cruciferae

Very large family containing many of our important vegetables such as : CABBAGE, MUSTARD, CAULIFLOWER, KOHLRABI, BROCCOLI, TURNIP, RADISH, WATERCRESS plus numerous flowers and weeds such as CANDYTUFT, WALLFLOWER, CARDAMINE and SHEPHERD'S PPURSE. 18 genera are in Nepal. Small flowers on a spike with 4 petals and 4 sepals plus long or flattened seed capsules make identtification of this family easy.

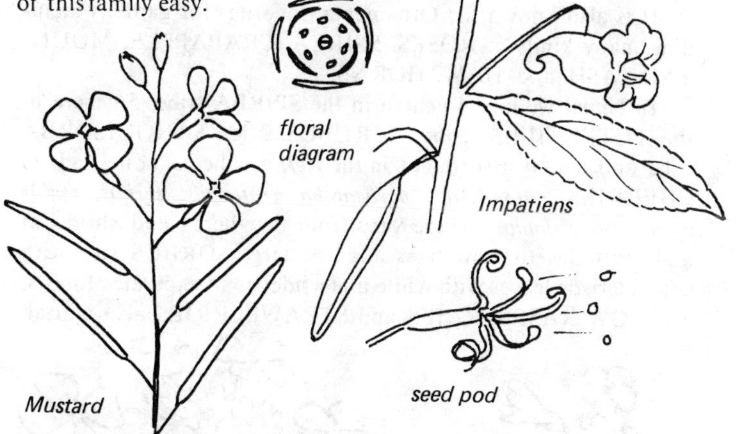

BALSAM FAMILY Balsaminaceae

This family of over 500 species is most common in trop. Asia and Africa. The one genus found in Nepal, *Impatiens* or TOUCH-ME-NOT is extremly diverse in the colors and forms of its speciees. These watery herbs are easily identified, however, by their irregular hanging flowers and the long seed pods which open explosively and throw out seeds when touched. Colors vary from white to yellow and blues & violets usually found in damp places, along streams at a wide range of altitudes.

FLAX FAMILY Linaceae

Flowers resemble Geranium and and Oxalis families but have 5 stamens rather than 10. 3 genera in Nepal: *Anisadenia*, *Linum* (FLAX) and *Reinwardtia* – the yellow SUNSHINE FLOWER. The BLUE FLAX is grown commercially for oil and fibers.

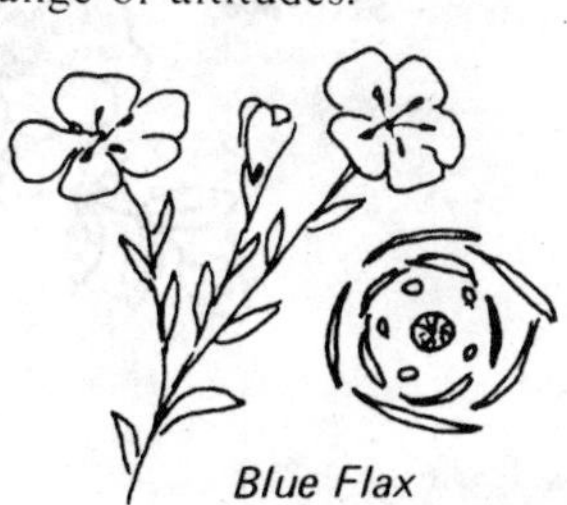

ROSE FAMILY Rosaceae

This is one of the largest and most important of the plant families. It includes over 2,000 species, mostly found in temperate regions. Typical flowers have 5 sepals, 5 petals and numerous stamens. The fruit is often fleshy.

Important fruits of this family include the STRAWBERRY, RASPBERRY, APPLE, PEAR, CHERRY, PLUM, PEACH, APRICOT, ALMOND and QUINCE.

It is also known for Ornamental favorites for gardens including many kinds of ROSES, SPIREA, CRABAPPLE, MOUNTAIN ASH and HAWTHORNS.

In Nepal we find 4 genera in the SPIREA tribe, 5 genera in the POTENTILLA tribe, 1 RUBUS 2 of SANGUISORBA tribe and a rich assortment in the ROSA tribe including WILD CHERRIES, *cotoneaster*, *pyracantha*, *crataegus*, *sorbus*, *malus* *pyrus* and *cydonia*. These vary from tiny herbs and shrubs at high altitudes to fruit trees and the large SORBUS tree with characteristic leaves with white undersides in temperate forests. YELLOW RASPBERRIES and STRAWBERRIES also appear.

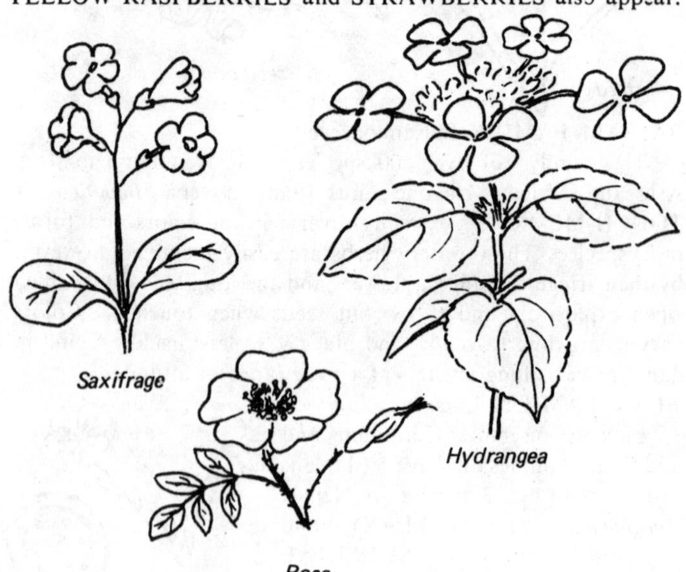

SAXIFRAGE FAMILY Saxifragaceae

Often succulent herbs generally found in temperate and cold regions. The flowers are similar in structure to members of the Rose Family but the number of stamens has been reduced to 4 to 5,or 8 to 10 and the carpels 1 to 3.Fruit is a capsule or berry. 5 genera in Nepal : *Astilbe, Parnassia, Tiarella, Saxifraga* and *Chrysoplenium.* The name means "rockbreaker" as these small plants often are found growing among the rocks in the mountains.

HYDRANGEA FAMILY Hydrangeaceae

This family is closely related to the Saxifrage Family. Members of this family are generally shrubs and trees often grown in gardens for their showy flowers. 4 genera are found in Nepal : *Hydrangea, Deutzia, Dichroa,* and *Philadelphus–*

Flowers with 5 lobed calyx and 4 or 5 petals. In *Hydrangea* genus, some Showy outer flowers may be steril.

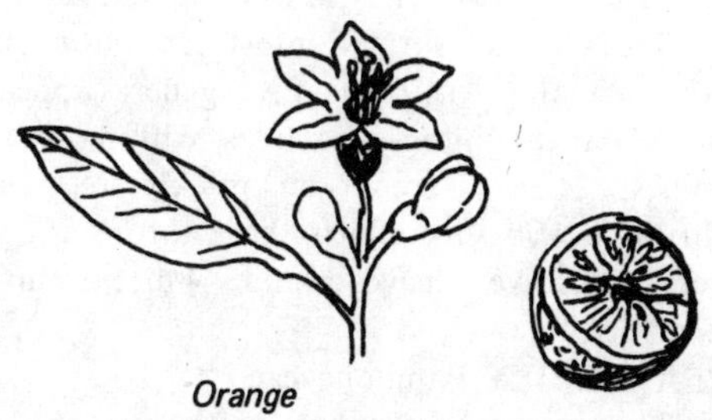

Orange

RUE or ORANGE FAMILY Rutaceae

Leathery aromatic leaves with translucent dots characterize this large and varied family of trees and shrubs. 11 genera appear in Nepal including the BEL FRUIT (*Aegle*). Various *Citrus* fruits are best known and economically important. TANGERINES so famous in Nepal have been grown commercially in midland hills. The AILANTHUS or Tree of Heaven of China falls in this group.

SENNA FAMILY Caesalpiniaceae

These are also mostly trees and shrubs. The flowers are more typically pea-like but may open wider and be less zygomorphic. 4 genera are found in Nepal : *Caesalpinia, Mezoneuron, Cassia,* and *Bauhinia* (the CAMEL'S FOOT trees and vines most common in lower tropical regions).

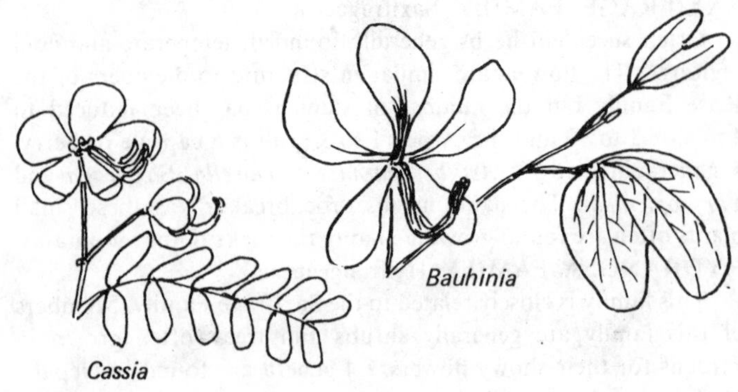

Bauhinia

Cassia

LEGUMES Leguminosae

This large group of over 13,000 species has been divided into three families. All have legumes or bean-like seed pods.

MIMOSA FAMILY Mimosaceae (Acacias)

Trees and shrubs most common in America and Australia. Five genera appear in Nepal : *Piptadenia*– trees with conical spines; *Acacia*—spiny or prickly trees or shrubs; *Mimosa*—which has throns and very sensitive leaves; and *Albizzia* an unarmed tree.

Mimosa

PEA FAMILY Papilionaceae

The remaining members of the Legume group include many herbs as well as trees and shrubs. Many important food plants are in this group including PEANUTS, SOYA BEANS, DAHL, PEAS, and various kinds of BEANS. If also includes some of our most striking ornamental trees such as GOLDENRAIN - LABURNUM, WISTERIA, and the FLAME TREE. The typical zygomorphous flowers and legume seed pods make this very large number of diverse species fairly easy to identify as a group. 52 genera of this

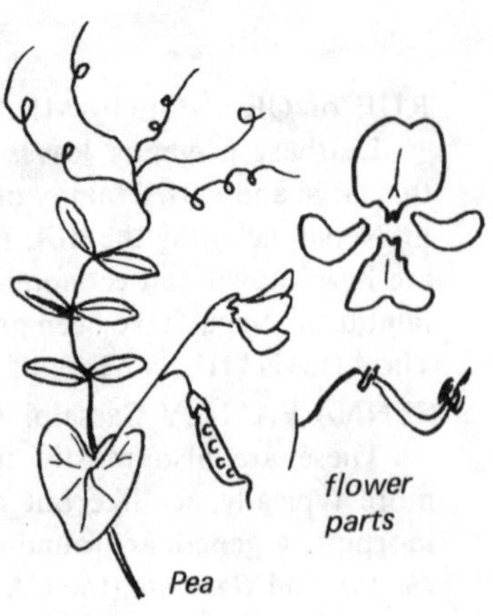

Pea

family are known to occur in Nepal. Some of the more interesting genera are : *Piptanthus* a Nepalese yellow laburnum, *Thermopsis* the almost black flowered pea of high altitudes, *Caragana* the prickly bush common in dry regions and the *Erythrina* and *Butea* with their bright red flowers in the tropical areas.

MYRTLE FAMILY Myrtaceae

The trees and shrubs of this family are mostly confined to Australia and the tropics. The leaves are generally thick and aromatic as they are dotted with glands. Many important plants producing edible fruits and aromatic oils are included in this group such as GUAVA, CLOVES, ALLSPICE and BAY RUM, BOTTLE BRUSH, EUCALYPTUS, and GUM trees of Australia have been introduced all over the world for fast-growing forest trees. 2 genera are native to Nepal : *Eugenia* (clove family), and Syzygium.

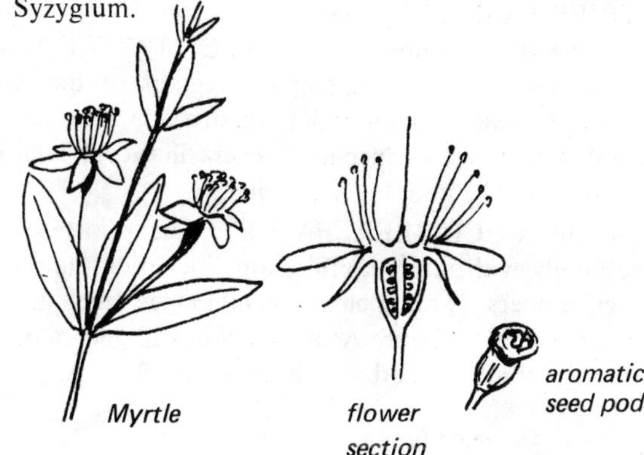

BEGONIA FAMILY Begoniaceae

Nepal has one genus, *Begonia* of this family which is well known for the improved varieties grown in pota and greenhouses. The 2, or 4 petaled flower and variegated leaves of this succulent plant are quite distinctive.

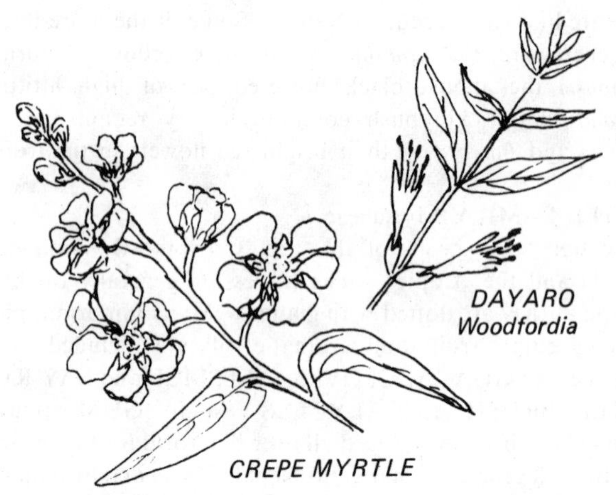

LOOSESTRIFE FAMILY Lythraceae

Trees, herbs and shrubs. The CREPE MYRTLE widely grown as an ornamental in subtropical regions of the world originated in the Indian region and Lagerstroemia also includes an important timber tree in Nepal. 4 genera in Nepal : *Rotala, Ammannia, Woodfordia* and *Lagerstroemia*.

PUMPKIN OR CUCUMBER FAMILY Cucurbitaceae

A large family with many useful plants including pumpkins, squashes, cucumbers, watermelons, cantaloupes and gourds. Cucumbers are native to South Asia. Nepal has 12 genera of this family – mostly climbing herbs with unisexual flowers.

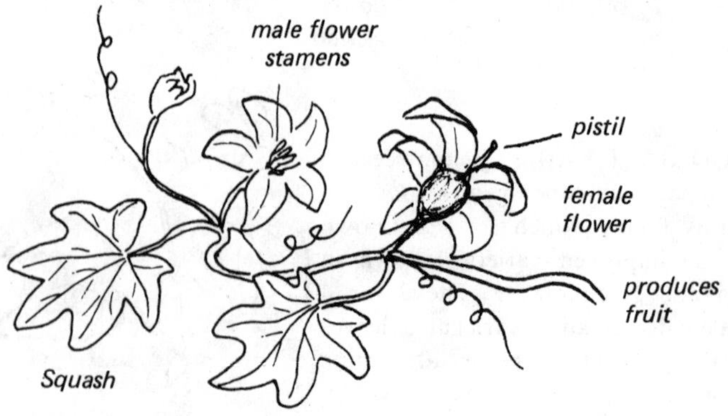

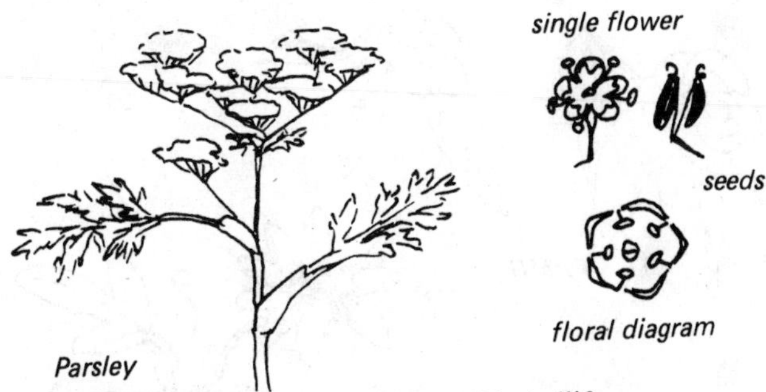

CARROT or PARSLEY FAMILY Umbelliferae

Biennial or Perennial herbs with hollow stems and large compound or dissected leaves, often with sheathing bases. Flowers in a simple or compound umbel and generally white.

Members of this family include CARROTS, FENNEL, PARSLEY, PARSNIP, CELERY, DILL, CARAWAY, ANISE, MYRRH and the very poisonous HEMLOCK !

20 genera have been reported from Nepal, including CARAWAY-*Carum,* ANISE-*Pimpinella,* CORIANDER-*Coriandrum* and COW PARSNIP-*Heracleum.*

CASHEW or SUMAC FAMILY Anacardiaceae

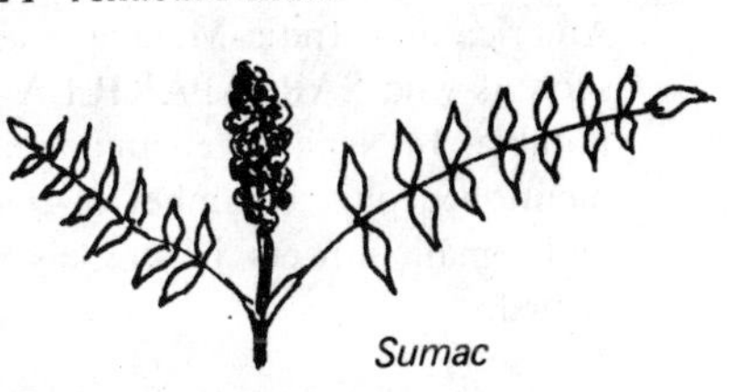

This interesting family includes the tasty MANGOS, CASHEWS and PISTACHIO NUTS. It also contains the *Rhus* genus which provides lacquers and fish poison. Some of them causes allergic blisters. In America some very poisonous plants are in this group: Poison Ivy and Poison Oak. The flowers are generally small and in racemes or spikes. The leaves often take on beautiful colors in the fall or as young leaves. 6 genera are known in Nepal *Rhus,* often with colorful red leaves, *Pistocia* (in the west), *Tapiria, Semecarpus, Mangifera* (the mango trees) and *Spondias.*

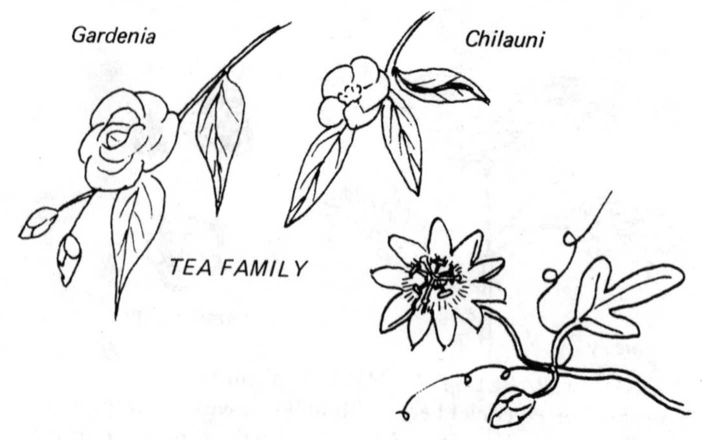

Passion flower

PASSION FLOWER FAMILY Passifloraceae

One genus *Passiflora* of this interesting family occurs in Nepal – a herbaceous climber with a distinctive clock-like face from which it gets its Nepali Name-Ghad Phul. Family is most common in tropical America.

GENSING FAMILY Araliaceae

Araliaceae tropical family (700 species centered in tropical America and India-Malaya. English Ivy *Hedera* and drug plants such as wild SARSAPARILLA *Aralia* and GINSENG *Panax* are notable. In Nepal 9 genera appear; the two herb families and vine mentioned plus a number of trees with very large plamate leaves and small flowers in umbels. Trees and shrubs are sometimes armed.

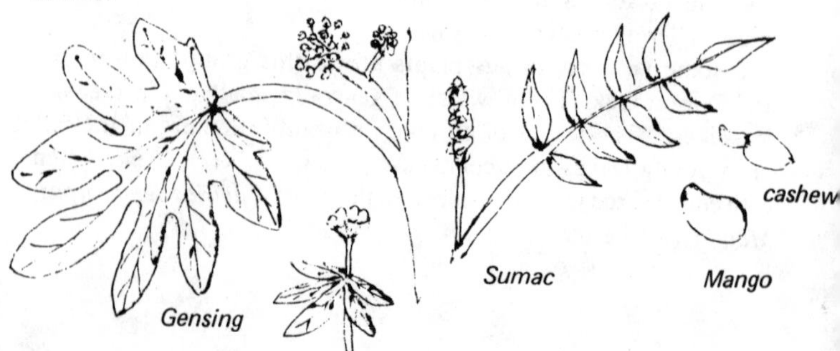

Gensing Sumac Mango

TEA FAMILY Theaceae

Known for the waxy, sweet smelling CAMELIA FLOWER this family also gives us our TEA. 4 genera are found in Nepal and tea is grown commercially in the eastern Himalayas. *Cleyera, Eurya, Schima* (CHILAUNE, the important forest tree) and *Camellia.*

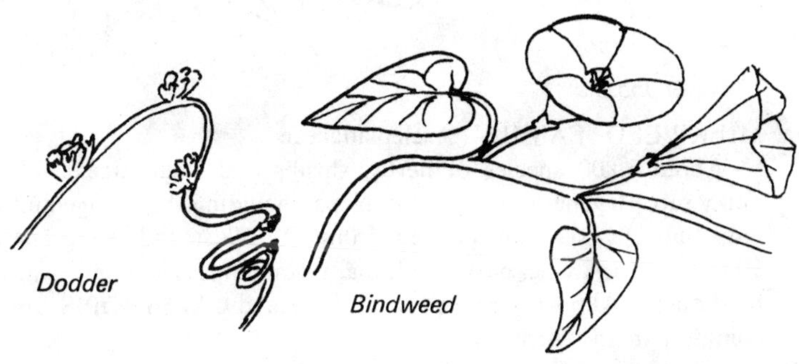

MORNING GLORY FAMILY Convolvulaceae

Large family of herbs, many of which are climbers. The petals form a funnel-shaped corolla and the 5 stamens are attached inside. The juice is sometimes milky, The SWEET POTATO is the most valuable member of this family. BINDWEED is widely found in cultivated fields. Parasitic DODDERS can be troublesome as they live on other plants. Ornamental species are highly prized for their showy flowers lasting but a day each. 9 genera are found in Nepal : *Cuscuta, Evolvulus, Ipomoca, Rivea, Argyreia, Porana, Convolvulus, Calystegia* and *Lettsomia.*

SPURGE FAMILY Euphorbiaceae

At least 7,000 species are in this extensive family. They all have a milky sap although they vary considerably in other ways, being trees, shrubs, herbs, or succulants. Small unisexual flowers are surrounded by showy leaves as in POINSETTIAS and CROWN-OF-THORNS or sometimes appear on a bright colored catkin as in the CHENILLE PLANT. The CASTER OIL PLANT yields the laxitive and TAPIOCA is grown for its edible roots. Some of the important RUBBER producing trees of Brazil are in this family (Hevea brasiliensis) 22 genera have been described for Nepal including *Euphorbia*, *Ricinus*, and *Croton*.

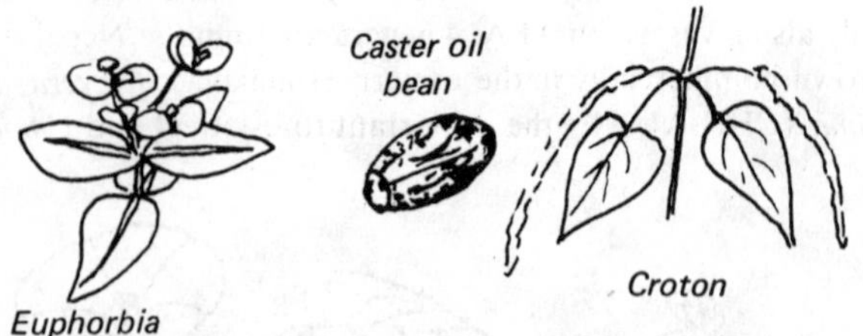

MILKWEED FAMILY Asclepiadaceae

About 1,800 species of herbs, shrubs and small trees with milky sap. 16 genera are found in Nepal including the orange and red butterfly-weed introduced from the West Indies. The HOYA BELLA vine, native to India, is sometimes found growing by houses. Almost treelike purple flowered CALSTROPIS are common in the Terai.

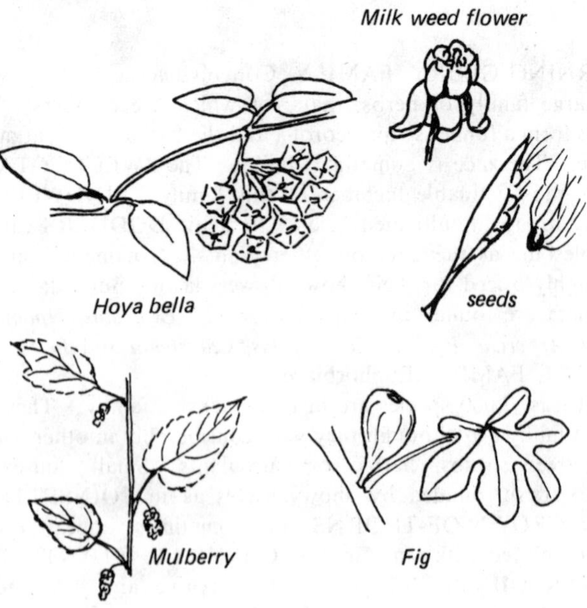

FIG or MULBERRY FAMILY Moraceae

Contains over 1,000 species of tropical and subtropical trees and shrubs. Milky latex and minute crowded unisexual flowers characterize this family. Many edible fruits such as MULBERRY, JACK FRUIT, BREADFRUIT, and FIGS are in this group. Many of the very large shade trees such as the BANYAN, PEPIL and INDIA RUBBER TREE are in the Ficus genus. 4 genera in Nepal : *Ficus, Morus, Cuadrania* and *Streblus.*

NETTLE FAMILY Urticaceae

Large family of herbs, some of which have stinging hairs on the leaves and stem. 13 genera in Nepal. The genus *Urtica,* although stinging, provides food and clothing to many people in isolated regions.

HEMP FAMILY Cannabinaceae

Represented by 1 genus in Nepal, the *Cannabis* used to make hashish and marijuana. The family also yields good fibers for cordage and oil is extracted from the seeds.

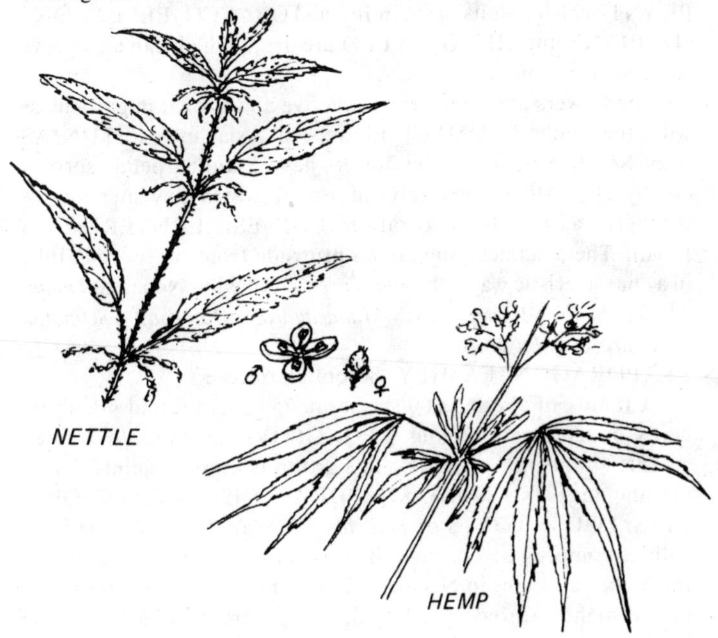

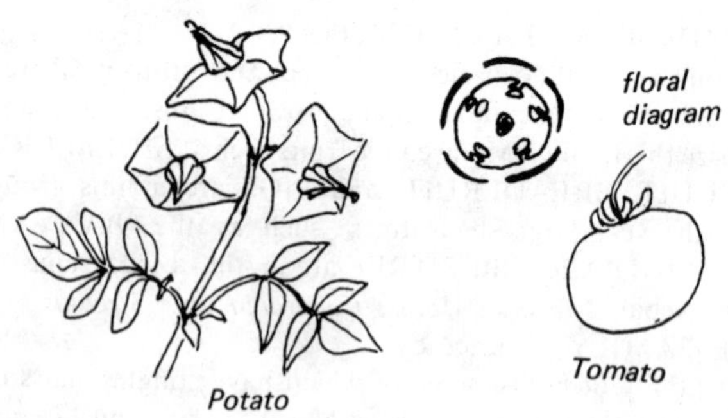

Potato

Tomato

NIGHTSHADE FAMILY Solonaceae

A family of over 2,000 species centered in Tropical America. Many of our important foods and drugs come from this important family which also contains many very poisonous plants. The POTATO, TOMATO, CHILI, PEPPER, and EGGPLANT are important foods, all originating in America except the EGG-PLANT which had its orgin in India. TOBACCO, BELLADONA, HENBANE and JIMSON WEED are drugs which can also prove to be very poisonous.

The flowers are often very attractive and grown in gardens as with the white TRUMPET Flower of Asia and PETUNIAS from South America. The flowers have 5 united petals surrou-ded by a persistent united calyx of 5 sepals which may later enclose the berry as in the decorative CHINESE LANTERN from Japan. The 5 stamens sometimes protrude from the corolla tube in a characteristic way. 8 genera are described in Nepal. *Solanum, Physochlaina, Hyocyamus, Mandragora, Daturoa, Scopolia, Nicandra* and *Physalis.*

SNAPDRAGON FAMILY Scrophulariaceae

A family of about 3,000 species in 75 genera found mainly as herbs in temperate regions. FOXGLOVE or *Digitalis* is used a heart stimulent, otherwise this group is known mainly for its ornamental plants such as SNAPDRAGONS and CALCEOLA-RIAS. LOUSEWORTS or *Pedicularis* are an Arctic-Alpine form with a compressed corolla. This group is well represented in the higher altitudes in Nepal. 32 genera of this family are found in the higher altitudes in Nepal. 32 genera of this family are found in Nepal including *Pedicularis* and *Scrophularia.*

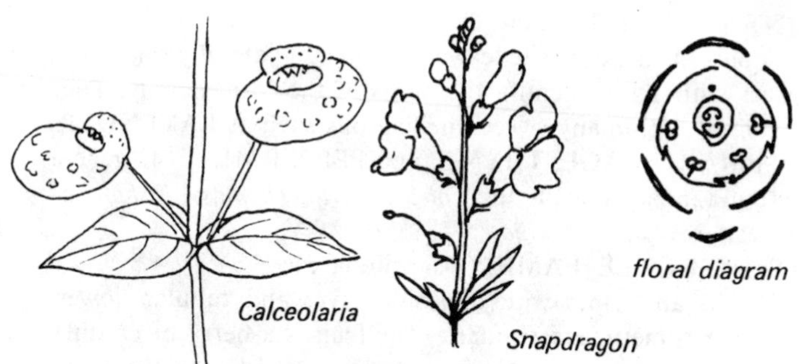

BIGNONIA FAMILY Bignoniaceae

The blue JACARANDA tree and orange TRUMPET VINE are prized ornamentals of the Bignonia Family grown in gardens everywhere. The 750 species of this family are mostly tropical trees, shrubs and vines. Their center is South America and only 3 genera grow wild in Nepal : *Amphicome* – red flowering herbs, *Stereospermum* and *Oroxylon* – both are flowering trees.

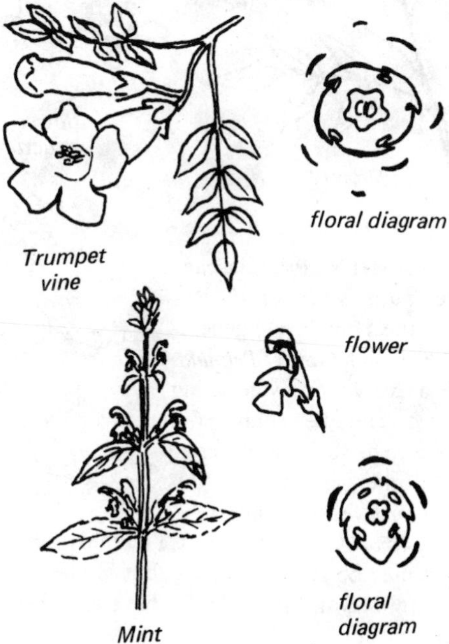

MINT FAMILY Labiatae

Square stems, opposite leaves and many bilaterally symetrical flowers with 2 lips identify the herbs of the Mint Family. They provide us with many sweet smelling oils such as LAVENDER, ROSEMARY, SAGE, THYME, and PEPPERMINT. 42 genera are found in Nepal including *Coleus, Salvia, Thymus, Elsholtzia*– a forest tree, and *Mentha.*

HONEYSUCKLE FAMILY Caprifoliaceae

Shrubs and vines with opposite leaves and tubular flowers which are sometimes irregular. The fruit is a berry or capsule. 6 genera are found in Nepal : *Sambucus* (ELDER), *Viburnum, Triosteum, Ablia, Leycestoria* and the thorny *Lonicera* of dry western Nepal. The ornamental SNOWBALL bush, SNOWBERRIES, and HONEYSUCKLE may be found in gardens.

Elderberry

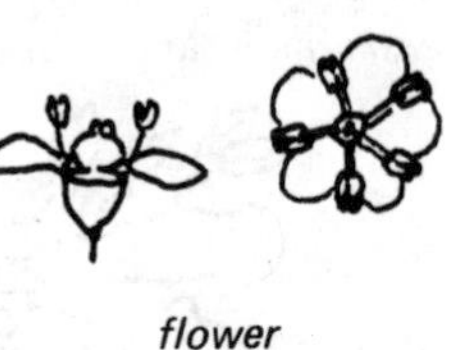

flower structure

PRIMROSE FAMILY Primulaceae

There are many varieties of Primula found in the Himalayas, generally above 6,000 ft. The lovely *Primula-dentata* has a very long blooming season and so can be found fall and winter as well as spring at different elevations. 4 other genera of this family are also in Nepal : *Androsace, Centunculus, Lysimachia* and *Angalis.* CYCLOMENS and SHOOTING STARS may be grown in pots but come from Europe and America. Himalayan PRIMROSES have also been introduced to western gardens.

Primula

GENTIAN FAMILY Gentianaceae

GENTIAN

The Gentian is a famous mountain flower which appears in a variety of species. Most bear blue flowers in the fall but a few flower in the spring. The tiny FAIRY GENTIAN may bloom most of the year and appears in grassy meadows as low as 3,500 feet. 8 genera are found in Nepal : *Limnanthemum, Exacum, Sebaea, Swertia, Halania, Gentiana, Cansora* and *Crawfurdia.*

OLIVE FAMILY Oleaceae

A family, widely distributed, but especially common in Asia and the East Indies. It contains 500 species in 20 genera. 7 genera are recorded in Nepal : *Olea* (OLIVE), *Jasminum* (JASMINES), *Fraxinus* (ASH), *Syringa* (LILACS), *Ligustrum* (PRIVET), *Nyctanthes* and *Osmanthus.*

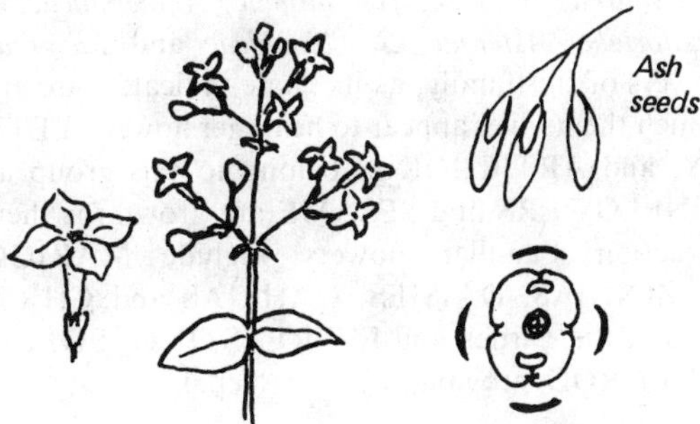

Olive family *floral diagram*

HEATHER FAMILY Ericaceae

A family of about 1,900 species found mostly in the cooler regions of the world. They require an acid soil generally. 7 genera occur in Nepal : *Rhododendron, Pyrola* (WINERGREEN with its blue berry and distinctive flavor), *Echinanthus* and *Pieris* (with rows of white bells), *Gaultheria, Diplarche* and *Cassiope.* Some are poisonous for grazing animals and others make bee's honey poisonous for humans. The Himalayas are especially famous

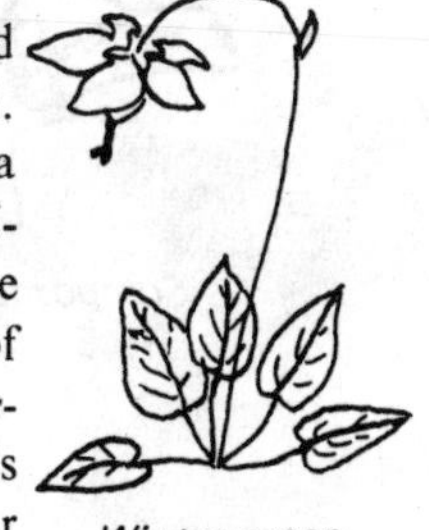

Winter green

for the number and variety of RHODODENDRON species. There are 32 in Nepal.

COMPOSITE FAMILY Compositae

The largest family of flowering dicotyledonous plants has at least 14,000 species in 900 genera. They are world-wide in distribution and include trees and shrubs in the tropics as well as the more common herbs in temperate regions. Nepal has 68 genera which have been divided into 11 tribes. *Cichoreae, Mutiseae, Cynareae, Inuleae, Heliantheae, Anthemideae, Vernonieae, Eupatorieae, Astereae, Senecionideae* and *Laggcrae*.

The flowers of this family, as its name indicates, are arranged in heads which themselves appear to be larger flowers. LETTUCE, CHICORY, and ARTICHOKES belong to this group as food plants. SUNFLOWERS and SESAME are grown for their seeds or oil extraction. Familiar flowers include MARIGOLDS, ASTERS, ZINNIAS, DAISIES, DAHLIAS and CHRYSANTHEMUMS of the garden and EVERLASTING, EDELWEISS, and GOLDENROD growing wild in Nepal.

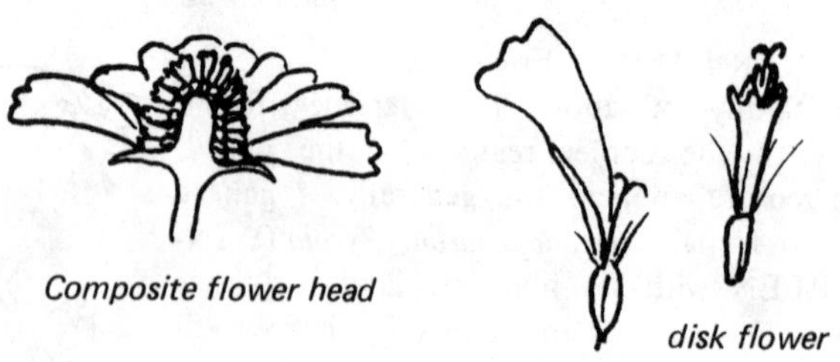

Composite flower head

disk flower

ray flower

0
500m.
1000m.
15 00 m.
2000 m.
2500 m.
3000 m.
3600 m.
4000 m.
4500 m.

Low. Tropical
Upp. Tropical
Low. Subtropical
Upp. Subtropical
Collineen
Montane
Low. Subalpine
Upp. Subalpine
Low. Alpine
Upp. Alpine

Gnetum montanum
Cycas pectinata
Podocarpus neriifolius
Pinus roxburghii
Abies pindrow
Cedrus deodara
Cupressus torulosa
Tsuga dumosa
Picea smithiana
Taxus baccata
Pinus wallichiana
Larix griffithiana
Abies spectabilis
Ephedra intermedia
Juniperus wallichiana
Juniperus recurva
Juniperus pseudosabina
Juniperus squamata
Juniperus recurva
Ephedra gerardiana

Vertical Distribution Of Gymnosperms In The Himalaya (After T.B. Shrestha 1974)

Forest vegetation in the Himalaya is almost always dominated by one or the other trees belonging to the following three families of plants, namely (1) Coniferae, (2) Cupiliferae (oaks, chestnuts), and (3) Ericaceae (Rhododendrons). Eastern Nepal, Sikkim, Bhutan and other areas in Eastern Himalaya are charecterised by evergreen broadleaved forests consisting mostly of oaks and rhododendrons. Western Nepal, Kumaon, Kashmir and other areas in Western Himalaya have large proportions of coniferous trees in the forest flora. Central Nepal, on the other hand, has to share more with the eastern flora than that of the west. Therefore, one goes anywhere in the Himalaya one is likely to find one or the other trees from the above mentioned families. Here we present three tables to help the readers in understanding the richness of species in those families and their range of altitudinal distribution.

SOME CONIFERS of the HIMALAYAS

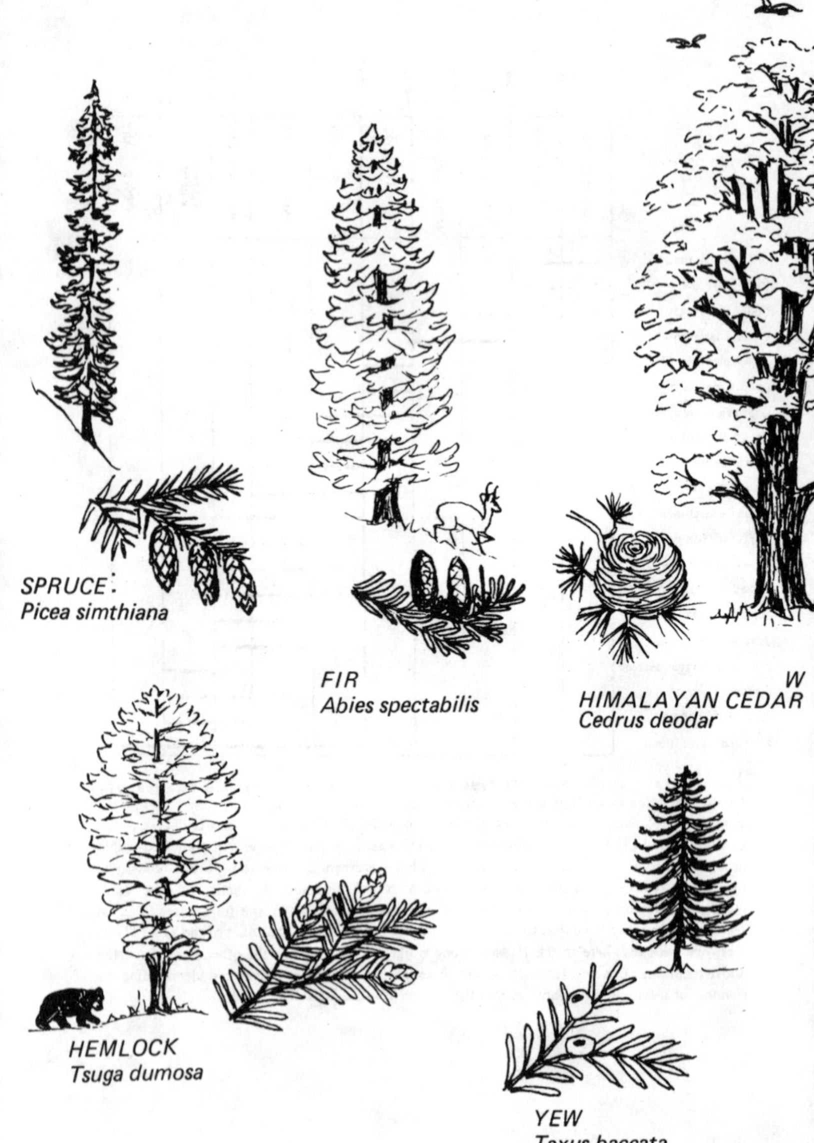

SPRUCE:
Picea simthiana

FIR
Abies spectabilis

HIMALAYAN CEDAR
Cedrus deodar

HEMLOCK
Tsuga dumosa

YEW
Taxus baccata

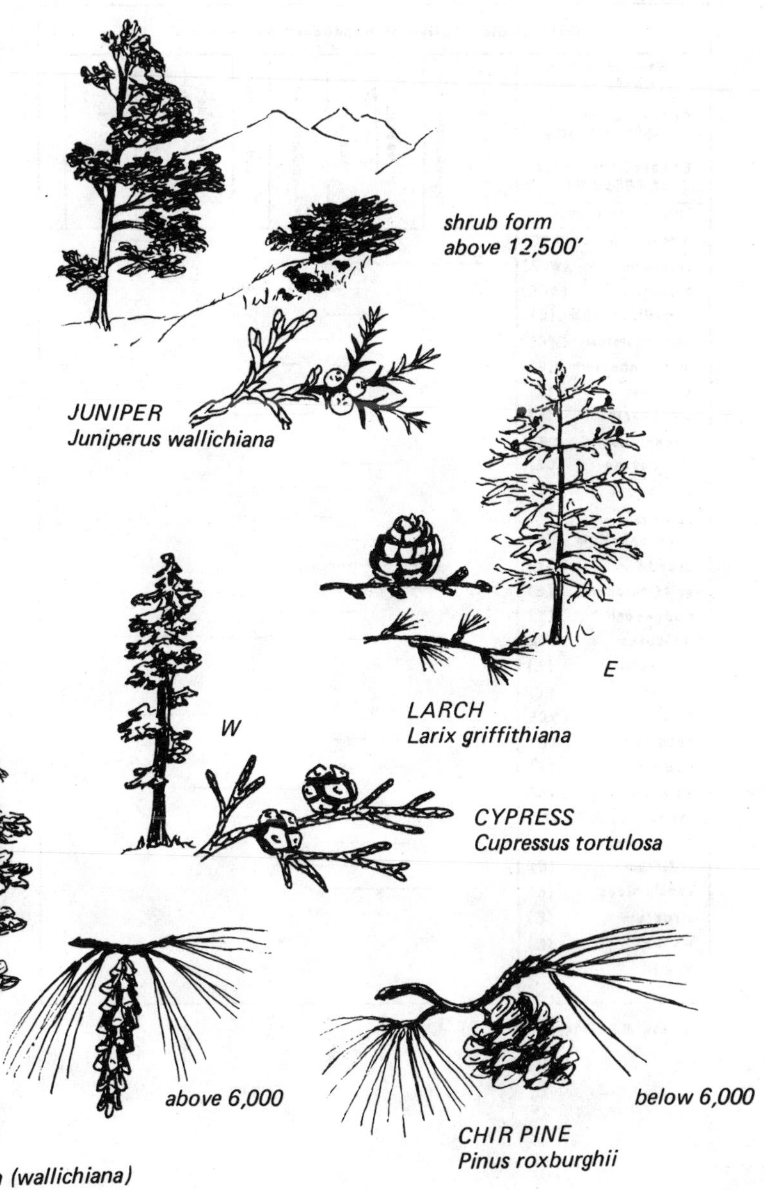
shrub form
above 12,500′
JUNIPER
Juniperus wallichiana
E
LARCH
Larix griffithiana
W
CYPRESS
Cupressus tortulosa
above 6,000
below 6,000
CHIR PINE
Pinus roxburghii
'E
lsa (wallichiana)

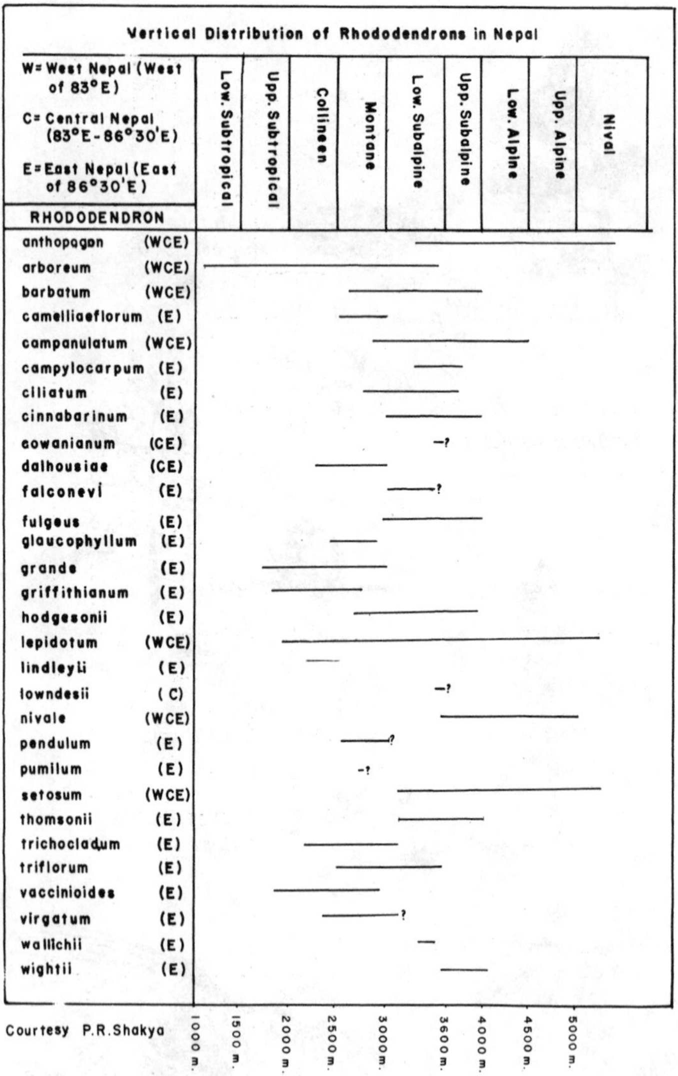

Vertical Distribution of Rhododendrons in Nepal

W= West Nepal (West of 83°E)

C= Central Nepal (83°E-86°30'E)

E= East Nepal (East of 86°30'E)

Low. Subtropical | Upp. Subtropical | Collineen | Montane | Low. Subalpine | Upp. Subalpine | Low. Alpine | Upp. Alpine | Nival

RHODODENDRON	
anthopogon	(WCE)
arboreum	(WCE)
barbatum	(WCE)
camelliaeflorum	(E)
campanulatum	(WCE)
campylocarpum	(E)
ciliatum	(E)
cinnabarinum	(E)
cowanianum	(CE)
dalhousiae	(CE)
falconevi	(E)
fulgeus	(E)
glaucophyllum	(E)
grande	(E)
griffithianum	(E)
hodgesonii	(E)
lepidotum	(WCE)
lindleyli	(E)
lowndesii	(C)
nivale	(WCE)
pendulum	(E)
pumilum	(E)
setosum	(WCE)
thomsonii	(E)
trichocladum	(E)
triflorum	(E)
vaccinioides	(E)
virgatum	(E)
wallichii	(E)
wightii	(E)

1000 m. | 1500 m. | 2000 m. | 2500 m. | 3000 m. | 3600 m. | 4000 m. | 4500 m. | 5000 m.

Courtesy P.R.Shakya

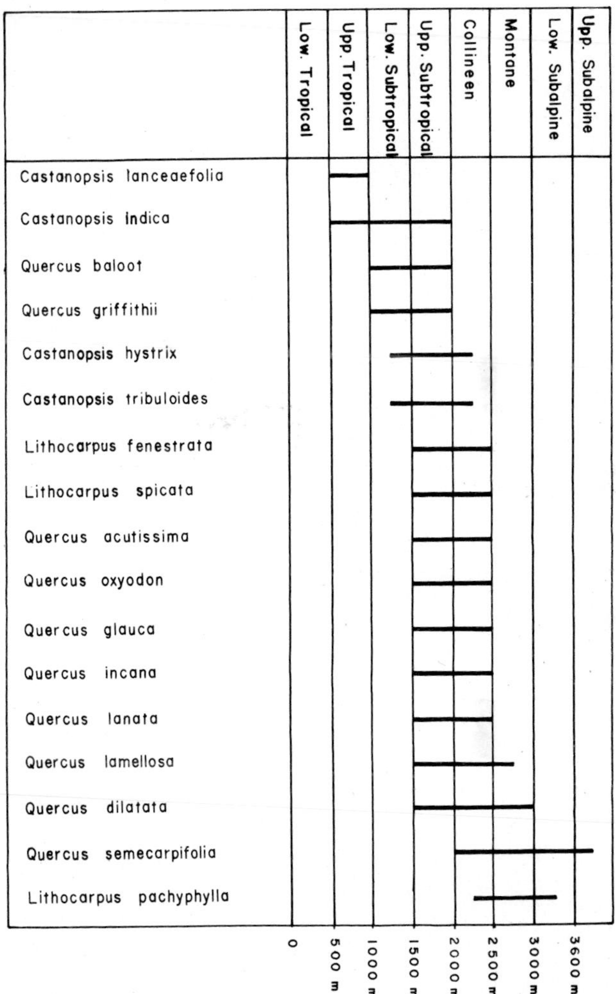

Vertical Distribution Of Oaks in The Himalaya (After Dobremez 1976)

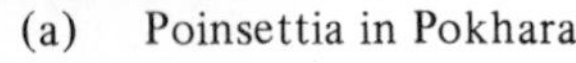

(a) Poinsettia in Pokhara

(b) Bottle Brush and Rana Statue

(c) Plumeria by Arun Valley house

(a) Bougainvillea

(b) *Grevillea robusta* "Silky Oak"

(c) *Wisteria*

(d) Crown of Thorns & Prickley Pear

(a) *Rhododendron arboreum* "Lali Guras"

(b) Color variations in Rhododendron

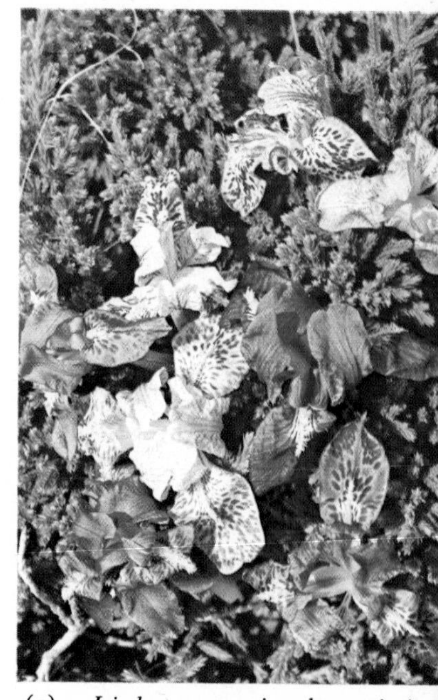

(c) *Iris kumaonensis* color variation

(a) *Primula* – "Primrose" color variations

Lilium nepalense "Nepalese Lily" (c) *Dendrobium densiflorum* "Sun Gava"

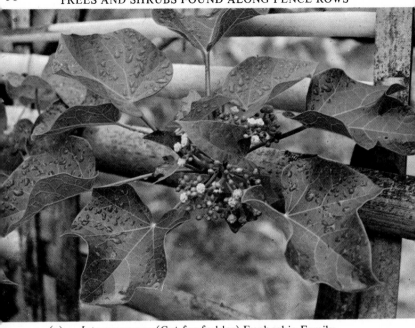

(a) *Jatropa curcas* (Cut for fodder) Euphorbia Family

(b) *Oroxylum indicum* "Tatelo"
Bignonia Family

(c) *Adhatoda vasica* "Asuro"
Snapdragon Family

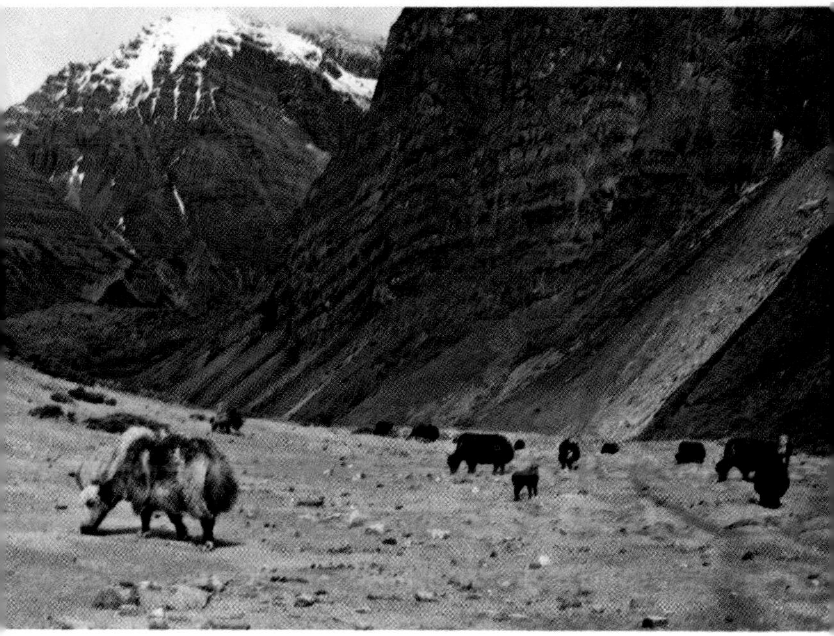

(a) Yaks in alpine pasture – 16,000 ft. Ringmo

(b) An Elephant in Sub-tropical grassland – 600 ft. Chitwan

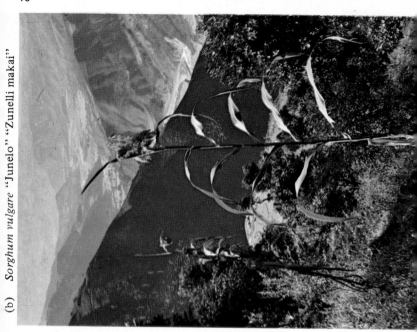

(a) Millet (*Elusine*) "Kodo" (Upper Trisuli)

(b) *Sorghum vulgare* "Junelo" "Zunelli makai"

Themeda – a lowland grass in Nepal

(b) *Thysanolaena maxima* Broom-grass of Nepal

) Barberry fence around wheat

(d) The rice plant

(e) Buckwheat and "Til"

(f) Millet and *Amaranthus* in Paro, Bhutan

MIDLAND FORESTS HAVE GIVEN WAY TO FARMS

(a) Suikhet, Pokhara valley 3,000 ft.

(b) Fields in Kathmandu 4,200 ft.

TERRACED HILLS FOR RICE

(a) Ghandrung in western Nepal

(b) Arun Valley in eastern Nepal

(a) Rice Harvest in Kathmandu Valley

(b) Winnowing barley in Langtang Valley

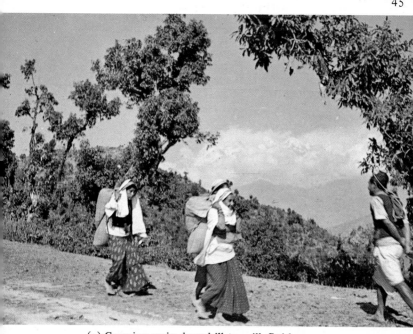

(a) Carrying grain downhill to mill, Pokhara

Mills on Stream near Kathmandu

(c) Millwheel in action

(a) Cattle graze in the forest

(b) New Settlers in Dolpo

(c) Fodder is cut from trees

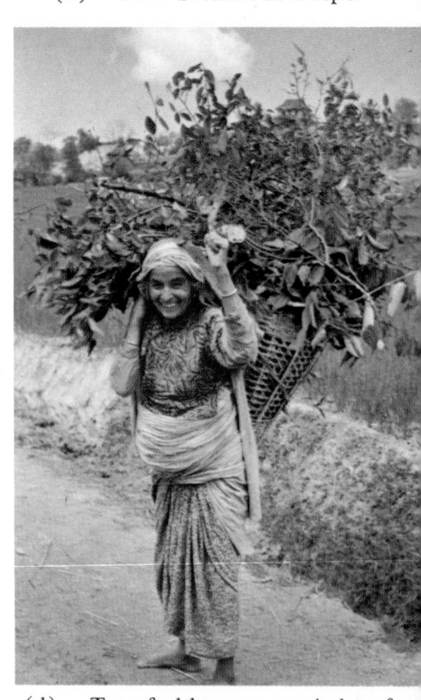

(d) Tree fodders are carried to farı

) Maize seedlings on rocky slope

(b) Cut and burned forests

(c) Rai family making temporary farm in hill forest

(a) Collecting thatch grass

(b) Carrying thatch

(c) Thatching roof

(d) Bamboo and thatched house

(a) Sugarcane press driven by oxen

(b) Sugarcane and Poinsettia

(c) Sugarcane press driven by men

(d) Sugarcane juice from press

(a) Tharu village with drying slices of cucumber

(b) Cucumber flowers

(c) Wild cucumbers "Kukur kankro"

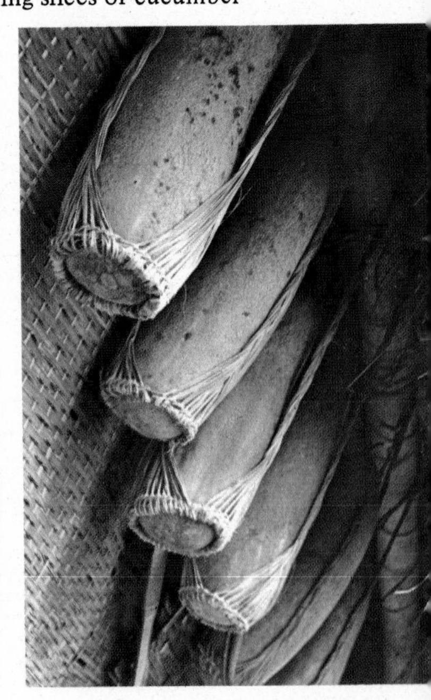

(d) Giant cucumbers stored under e

(a) Armala – Gurung village in Pokhara region

(b) Deserted rammed-earth house in *Amaranthus* field Bhutan

(a) *Datura suaveolens* – beautiful but poisonous Trumpet Flowers

(b) Small potatos at market

(c) Red Peppers being dried

(SOLANACEAE)

(a) Kantakari flowers

(b) Kantakari berries

(c) Tobacco Plant *Nicotiana tabacum*

Physalis peruviana – Lantern Plant

(e) *Datura stramonium* sacred to Shiva

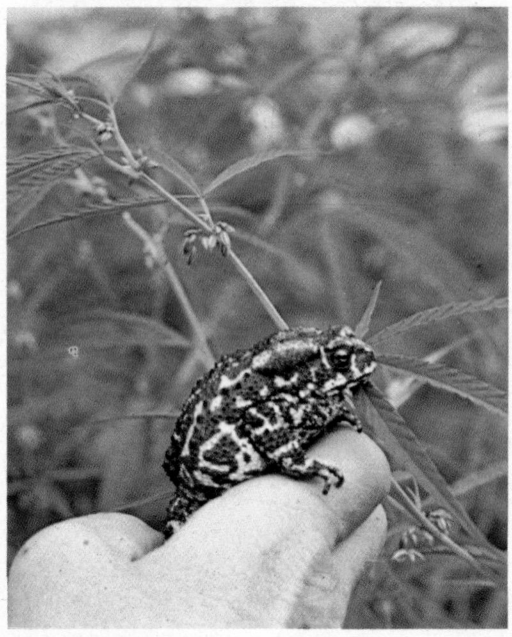

(a) Hemp behind native toad

(b) *Urtica dioca* – Common Nettle

(c) *Girardinia palmata* – Hill Nett

.) Mustard oil press – Mustard oil is the main cooking oil of the Midlands.

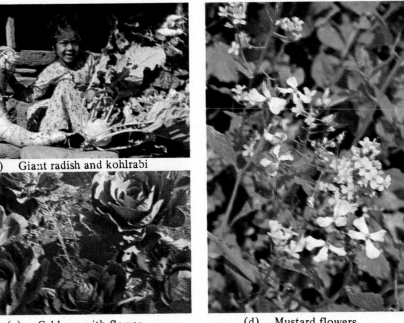

) Giant radish and kohlrabi

(c) Cabbage with flower

(d) Mustard flowers

(a) Gortzebra Valley – Center for sheep raising in Jumla District

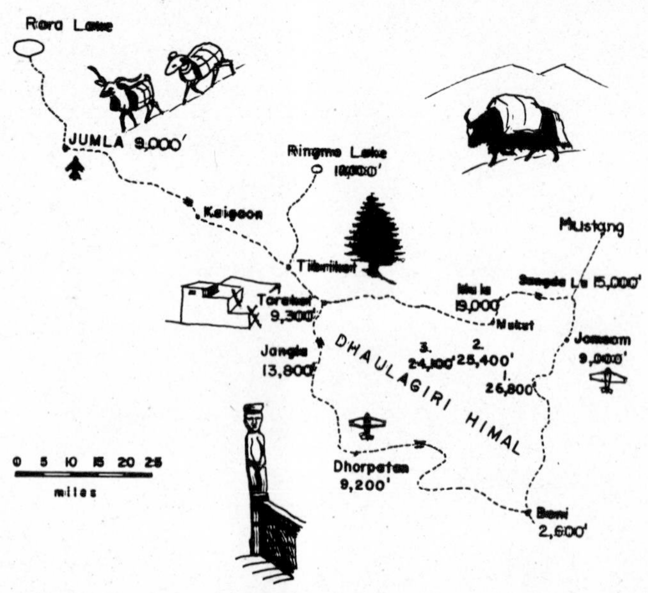

(b) (map of area)

(a) Mikot Village – west side of Dhaulagiri

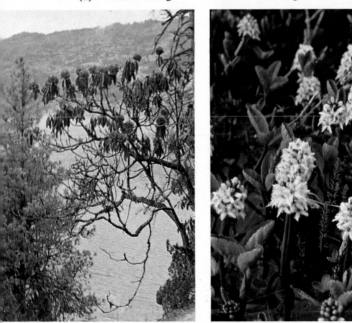

Rara Lake – Pine and Rhododendron

(c) Bog Bean *Menyanthes trifoliata*

(a) *Cedrus deodara* – the Himalayan Cedar

b) *Picea smithiana* – the Himalayan Spruce

(c) Spruce cones hang down from b

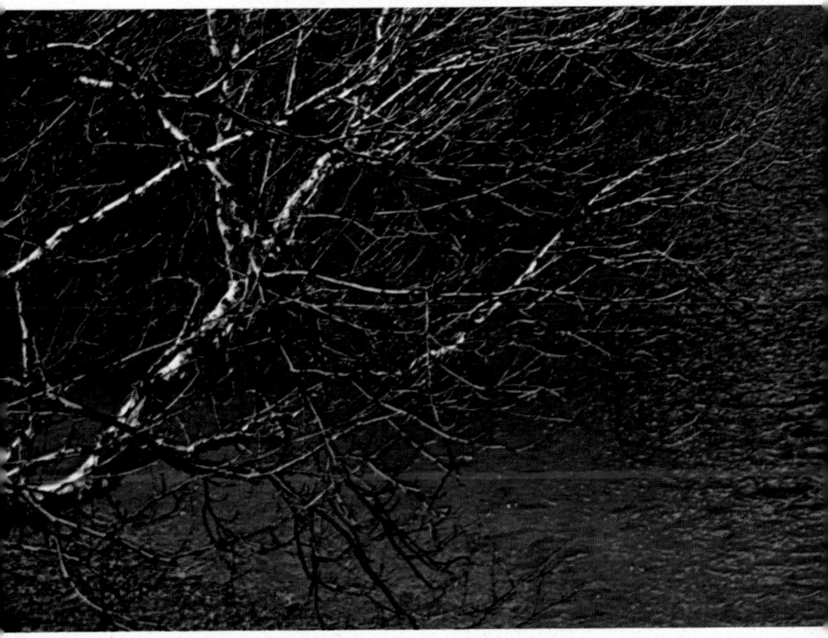

(a) *Betula utilis* – the White Birch by Phoksumdo Lake

(b) Phoksumdo tal 12,000 ft.

(c) *Buddleia tibetica* is sweet scented

Kanjiroba Himal and coniferuous forest

(a) Catkins of *Populus ciliata*

(b) South Dolpo mixed forest

(c) Maple seedlings

(d) *Primula* and *Daphne* flowers

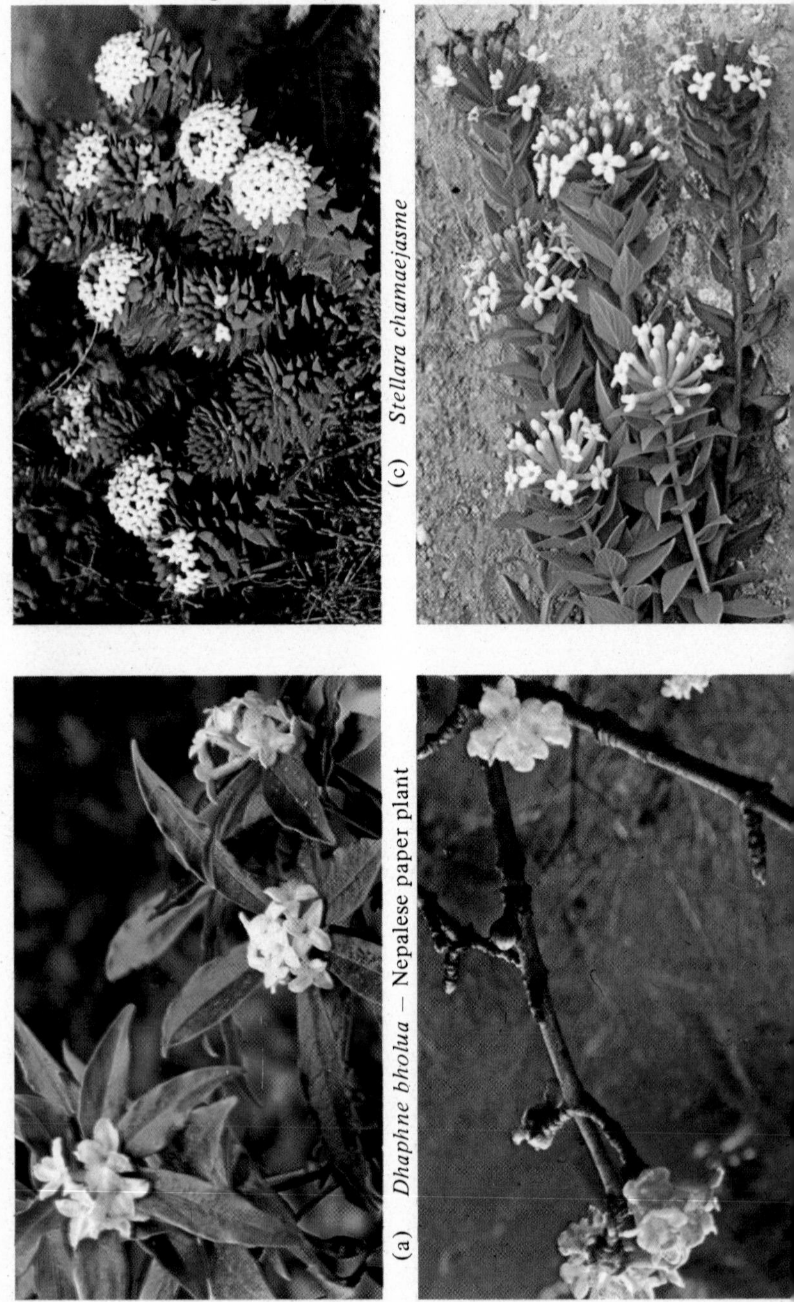

(c) *Stellara chamaejasme*

(a) *Dhaphne bholua* – Nepalese paper plant

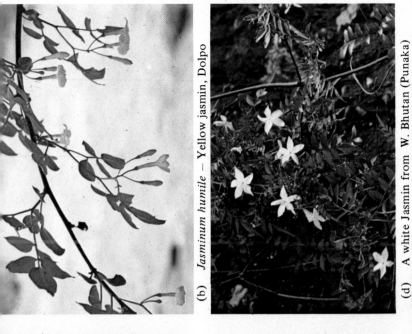

(a) *Leptodermis* resembles *Daphne*

(b) *Jasminum humile* – Yellow jasmin, Dolpo

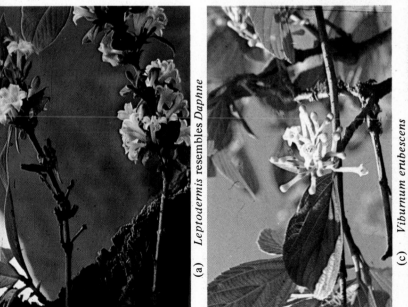

(c) *Viburnum erubescens*

(d) A white Jasmin from W. Bhutan (Punaka)

(a) *P. strumosa* and *P. denticulata*

(b) Petiolaris Primula

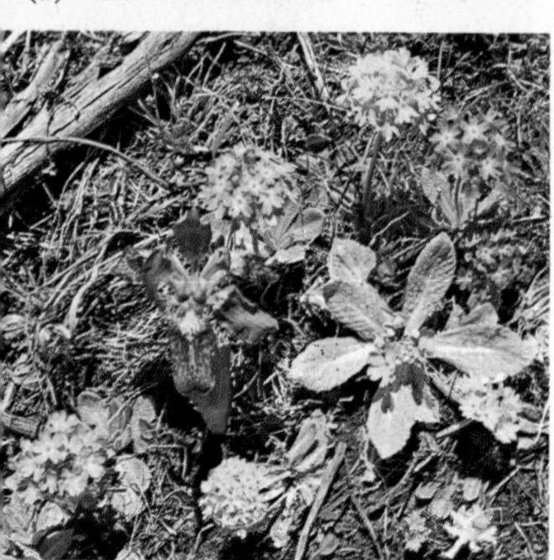

(c) Variety of Primulas with iris

(d) *Primula denticulata*

(e) Yellow Primrose *Primula strumosa*

(f) White Primrose – *Primula obli*

Gentian by *Androsace* cushion

(b) *Saxifraga* grows like *Androsace*

) *Androsace* – loose spray

(d) *Androsace* – compact cushion

Androsace – when high and dry

(f) *Primula* at about 9,000 ft.

(a) Mountain Clematis *Clematis montana* near Rara Lake

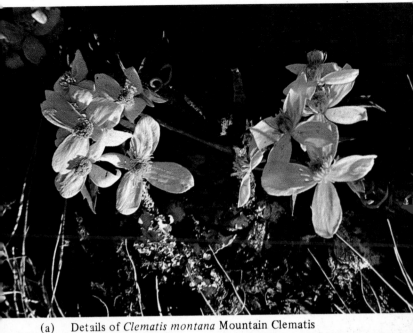

(a) Details of *Clematis montana* Mountain Clematis

Lavender vine in Arun Valley

(c) *Clematis acutangula* – Paro, Bhutan

(a) Mulah Pass at 19,000 ft. looking south to Dhaulagiri II

(b) Dhaulagiri *II* from Mukut region

(c) Tibetan Plateau – 16,000 ft., Mula

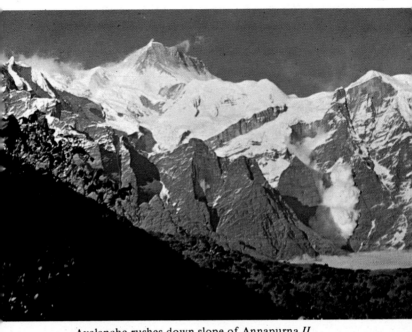

Avalanche rushes down slope of Annapurna *II*

(b) Annapurna *II* from Marsyangdi Valley

Landslide between Ghasa and Leyte

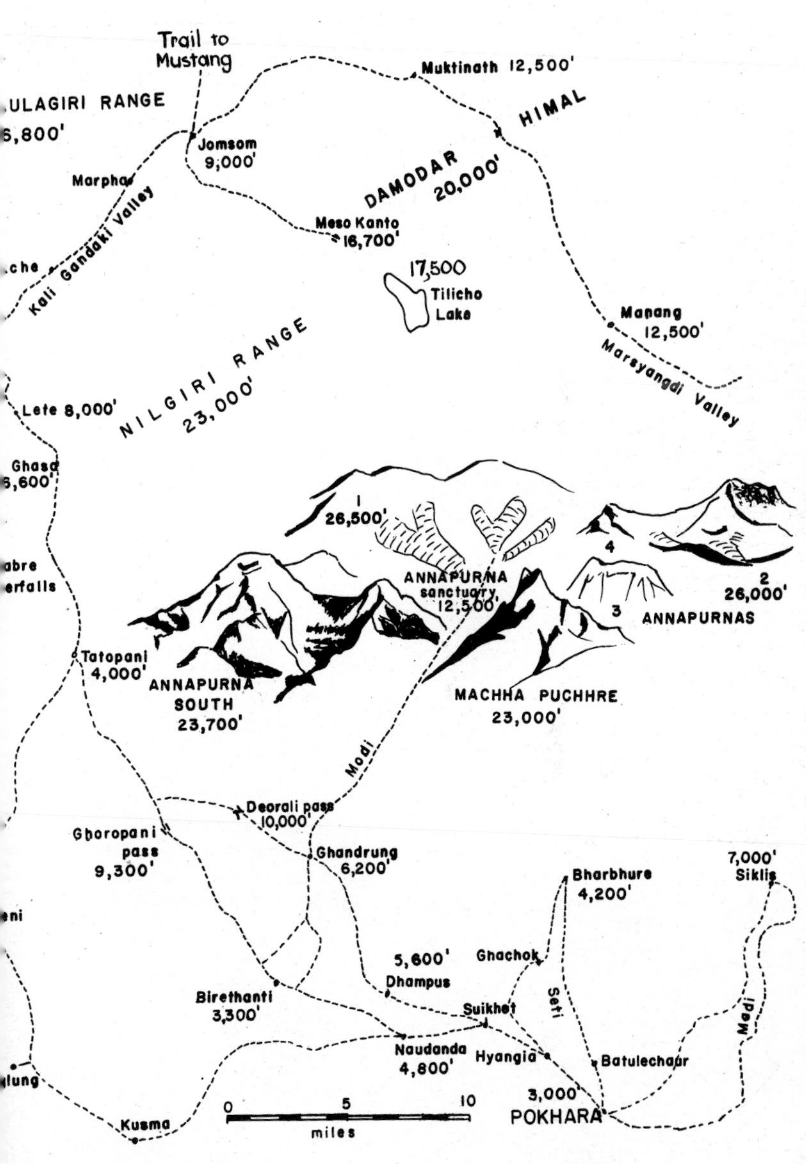

(map – Pokhara and north)

THE UPPER KALI GANDAKI IS ALSO A DRY REGION

(a) Folded rocks above Jomsom – Junipers

(b) Dzarkot village in Muktinath Valley – Poplar trees

(a) *Caragana brevispina* is common in Arid regions

Detail of *Caragana* showing spines

(c) Nilgiris and white desert roses

(a) Yak in the high and dry zone near Tilicho Pass 14,000 ft.

(b) Dhaulagiri and Tukuche Peaks from near Leyte

(a) *Lonicera spinosa* – Mukut

(b) *Oxygraphis* on Damphe Pass

(c) Alpine Buttercups

(d) Alpine *Astragalus*

) Blue Prickly Pea – *Astragalus*

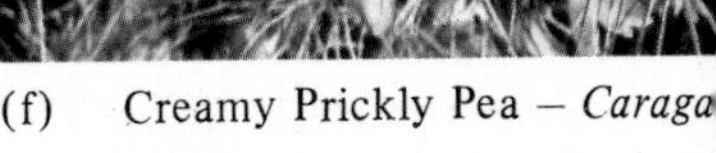

(f) Creamy Prickly Pea – *Caraga*

Some Euphorbias and the Compositae have aggregated flowers–

a) *Euphorbia himalayensis* from W. Nepal

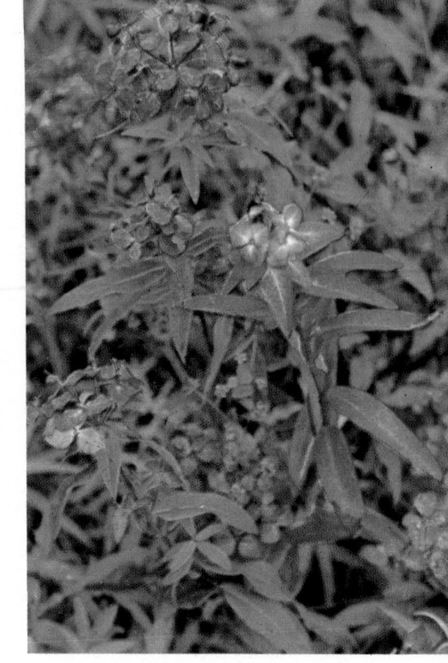

(b) *Euphorbia wallichii* from Bhut

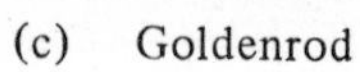

(c) Goldenrod

(d) Sunflower grown in Paro, Bhutan

(a) Close up of *Ainsliaea pteropoda* – Flowerhead has 4 simple flowers.

b) Twin plants of *Ainsliaea*

(c) Wind-blown seeds of compositae

Marrue Sunflower, a giant of compositae

(a) Daisys on Naudanda Ridge – Annapurnas behind

(b) Daisys and Poincettias at Gantok, Sikkim

SOME MEMBERS OF COMPOSITAE

(a) *Tragopogon*

(b) *Lactuca* 'Chicory"

(c) Pink Daisy

(d) Senecio

(e) Butterweed (center)

(f) Everlasting

(a) The Chir Pine in Trisuli Valley (*Pinus roxburghii*)

The Chir Pine and its bark

(c) Blue Pine (*Pinus wallichiana*)

(a) *Rosa sericea* – 4 petaled rose

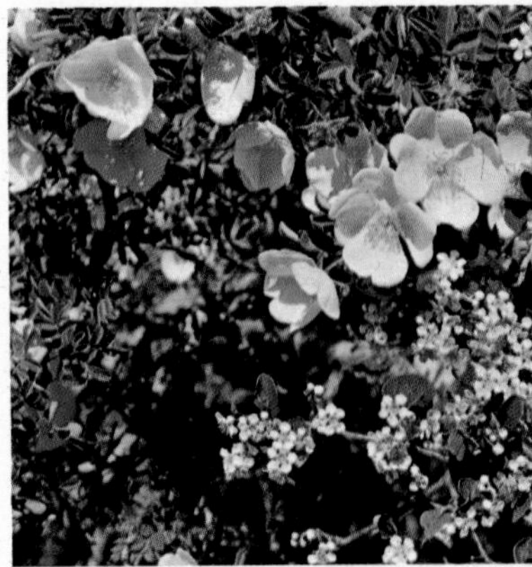

(b) *Rosa sericea* and *Cotoneaster* grow together

(c) Himalayan Strawberries

(d) *Rosa moschata* "Wild Musk R

(e) *Sorbus cuspidata* "Beam"

(f) *Prinsepia utilis* "Dhatelo"

(a) Apricot grown in upper Kali Gandaki Valley

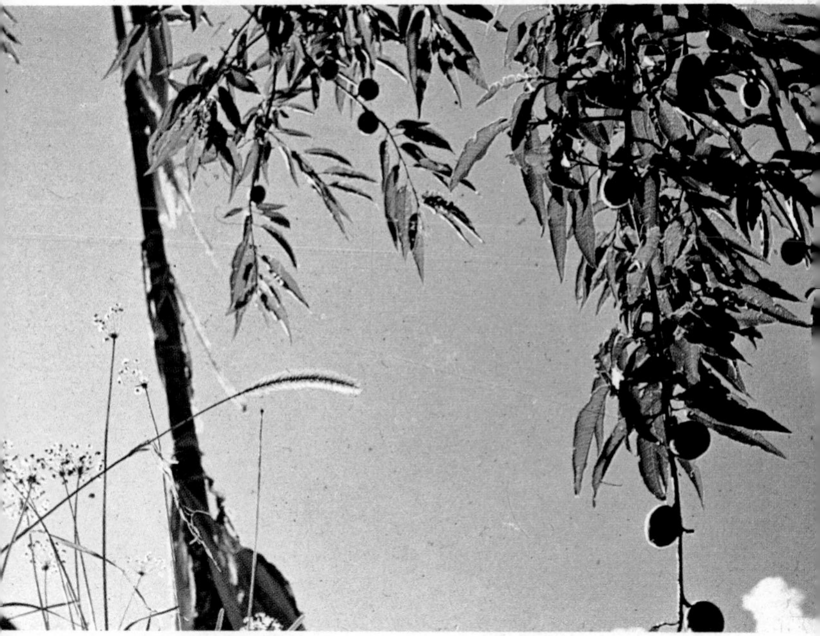

(b) Apricots and wild onions in W. Nepal

The fish-tail see from Modi River

(a) Above sea of clouds from east (above Siklis)

From the South (upper Seti)

(c) From the west (Hinko)

FROM ANNAPURNA SANCTUARY

(a) Hiunchuli and Annapurna I enclose the Annapurna Sanctuary

(c) The Site of Annapurna Sanctuary seen from Pokhara Valley

Some varieties of *Iris*

(a) From Marysangdi Valley

(b) From Solu Khumbu

(c) Marysangdi Valley near Chame is forested.

(a) Wooded slopes as seen from the south

(b) Bare slopes as seen from the north

(b) Pink *Luculia gratissima* with (a)

(a) *Thunburgia coccinea* vine

(a) *Osbeckia* sp.

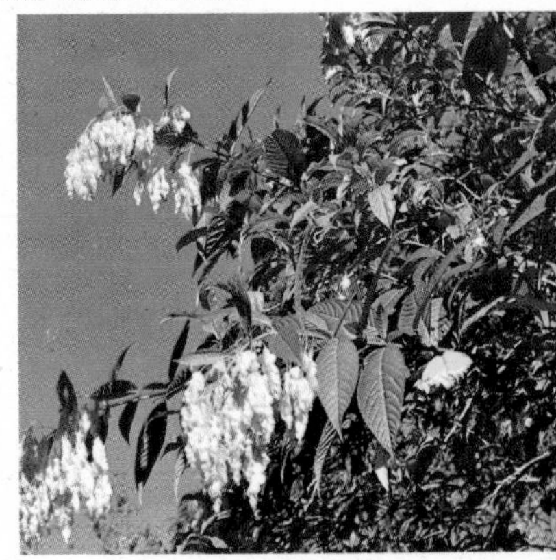

(b) *Dobinea vulgaris,* Ash family

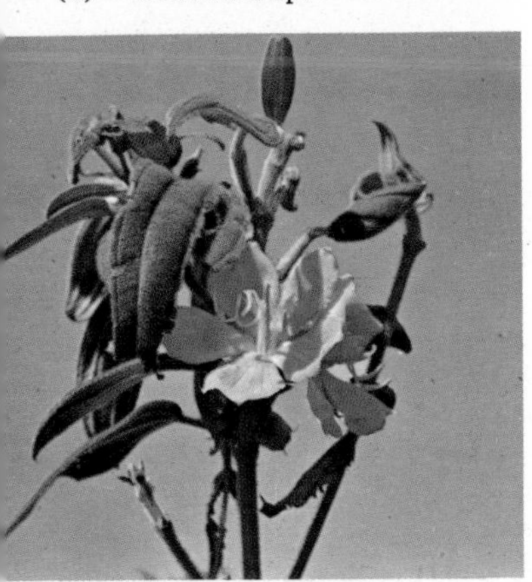

(c) *Osbeckia detail*

(d) Chilaune tree above Phewa Tal

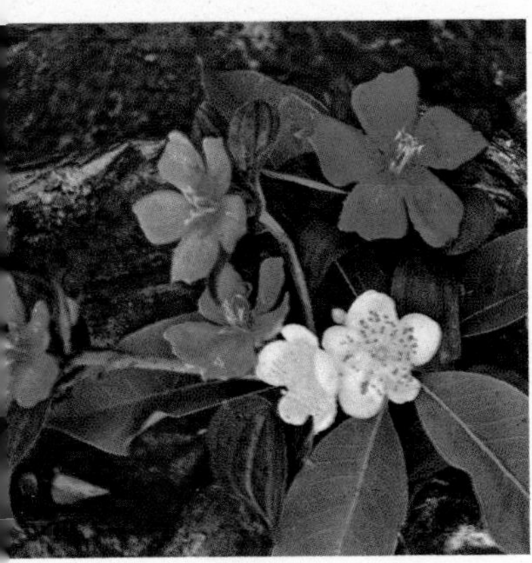

) Chilaune and *Osbeckia* flowers

(f) Chilaune – *Schima wallichii*

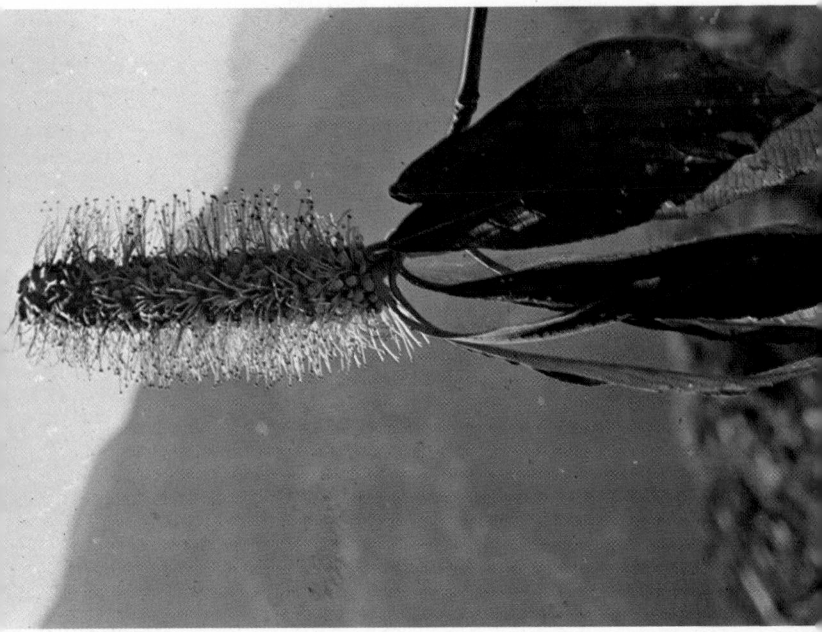

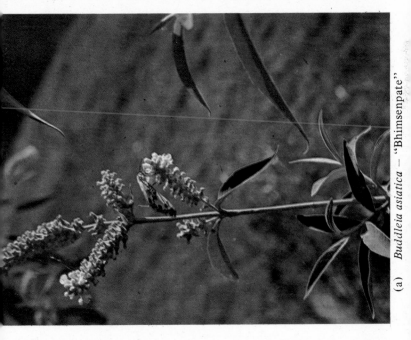

(a) *Buddleia asiatica* – "Bhimsenpate"

(b) *Caryopteris* – "Nilo Bhusure"

BERRIES ARE PRETTY BUT NOT ALWAYS GOOD TO EAT

(a) Blue *Dichroa febrifuga* held by Nani

(b) *Smilax* vine with berries "Kukur

(c) *Paris polyphylla* – "Satwa"

(d) *Paris* pods have showy seeds

(a) *Maesa chisea* flowers and berries

Arisaema tortuosa 'Sarpa makai'' or snake corn

(c) Various Aroids of Nepal

(a) *Arisaema tortuosa*

(b) *Remusatia vivipara*

(c) *Arisaema griffithii* "Cobra Plant"

(d) Aroid with spathe over 15 inche:

(a) *Aconitum spicatum* "Monk's Hood" the "Bikh"

(b) The Gentian vine

SOME OAKS OF NEPAL

(a) *Quercus semecarpifolia* with *Usnea* lichens – "Banjh"

(b) Same close up

(c) *Castanopsis indica* – Chestnut

(d) *Quercus lamellosa* – "Bansi"

a) *Populus ciliata* "Lekh Pipal", the only broad-leaved tree in Muktinath

(b) Horse Chestnut
Aesculus indicus "Naru"

(c) Poplar tree near Marpha

(b) Barberry's colored leaves

(a) *Berberis asiatica* "Chutro" fruits are edible

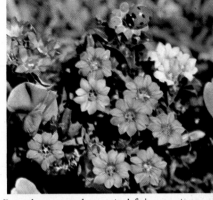

Thumbnail size bouquet– (b) *Parochaetus* and assorted fairy gentians

Associates with fairy gentians

(d) *Delphinium* from Bhutan

Corydalis cashmiriana on birch bark

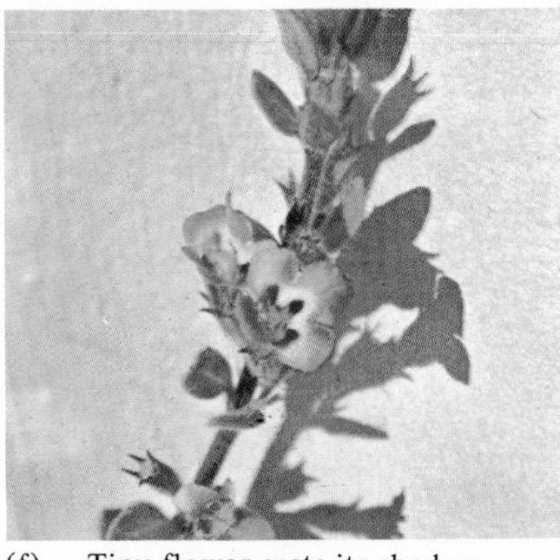

(f) Tiny flower casts its shadow

(a) "Simal" flower *Salmalia malabaricum* (b) Simal tree or Silk Cotto

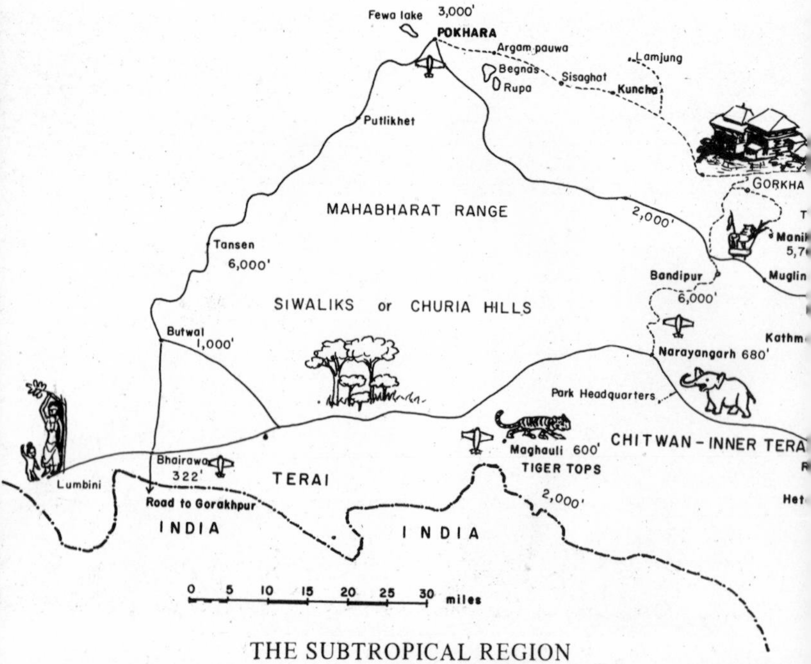

THE SUBTROPICAL REGION

Oxcarts near Lumbini, birth-place of Buddha

(b) Sunset at Lumbini

Erythrina stricta "Phaledo" flowers

(b) "Phaledo" tree *Erythina stricata*

Erythrina arborescens – Coral Bean

(e) *Butea minor*

(f) *Butea frondosa* "Palas"

(a) *Bauhinia variegata* "Koiralo" tree – The flowers are eaten.

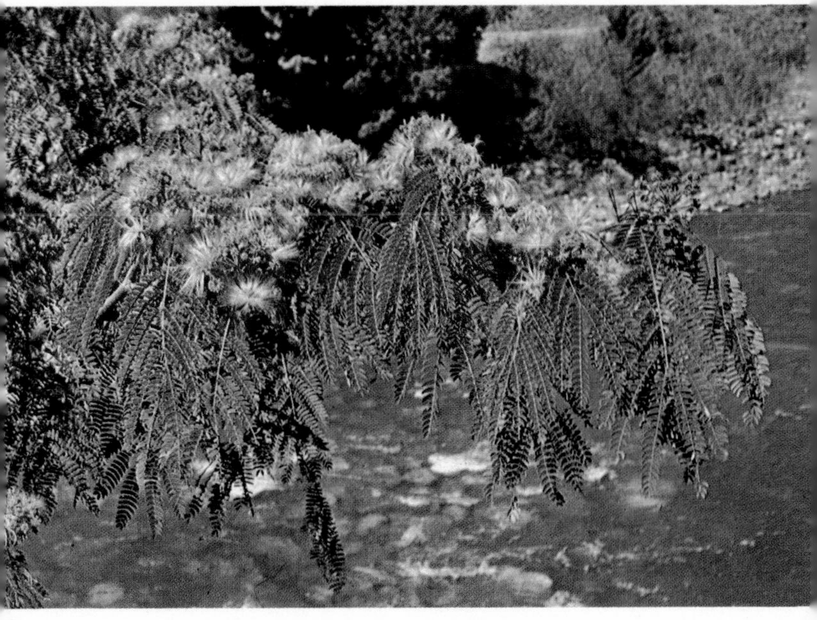

(b) *Albizzia mollis* "Siris" tree

SAL ARE THE GREAT LUMBER TREES OF NEPAL

(a) Sal leaf plate "tapari" and some seeds

(b) *Shorea robusta* "Sal" trees in flower

Making plates from Sal leaves

(c) *Lobelia pyramidalis* flowers "Eklebir"

Sal forest in Chitwan

(d) *Lobelia pyramidalis* plant

(a) *Dillenia* and semi-deciduous forest

(b) *Bauhinia* vine on Sal trees

(c) View from Tiger Tops Lodge

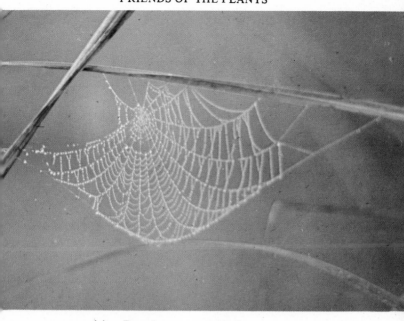

(a) Dew drops on a spider's web

(b) Garden spider

(c) Lizard surveys the scene

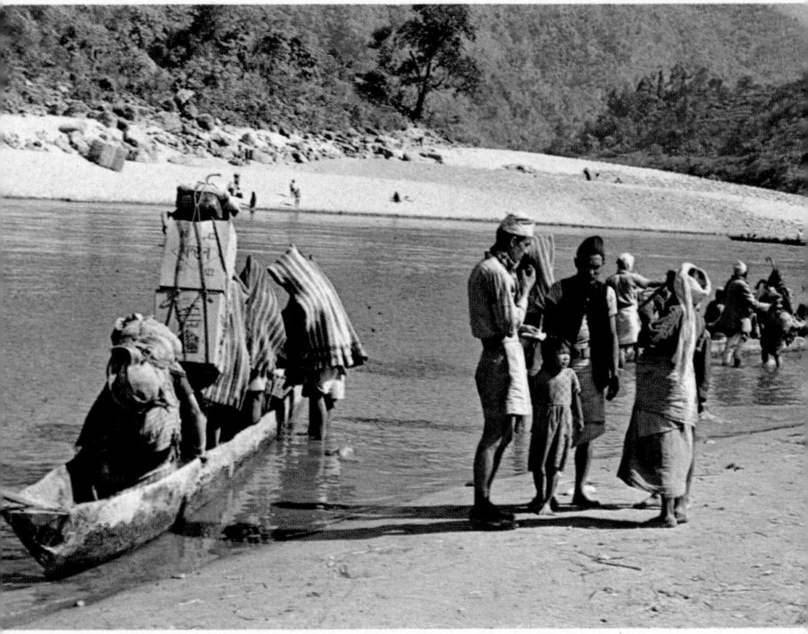

(a) Canoe crossing on way to Rapti Valley

(b) Gurung girls settled in Chitwan

ɔmoea fistulosa Morning Glory bush

(b) *Azolla imbricata* Duckweed

'pomoea palmata Railway Creeper

(d) *Porana grandiflora* Bindweed

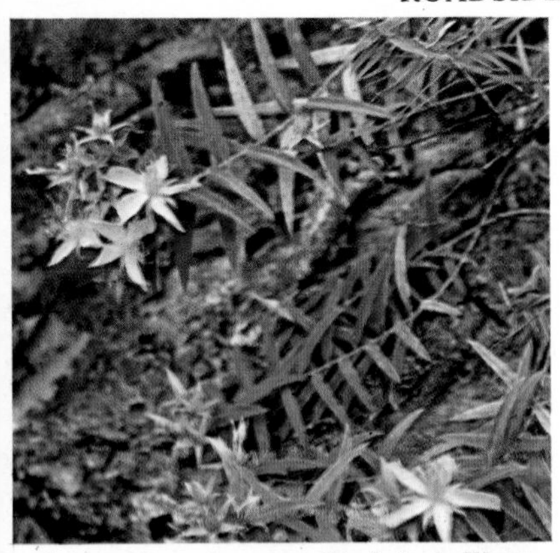

(a) *Hypericum* or St. John's Wort

(b) *Reinwardtia trigyna* – "Py

(c) *Calotropis gigantea* – "Aak"

(d) Sumac's red leaves

(e) *Colquhounia coccinea*

(f) *Woodfordia fruticosa* – "Dhair

lebrookea oppositifolia "Dhusure"

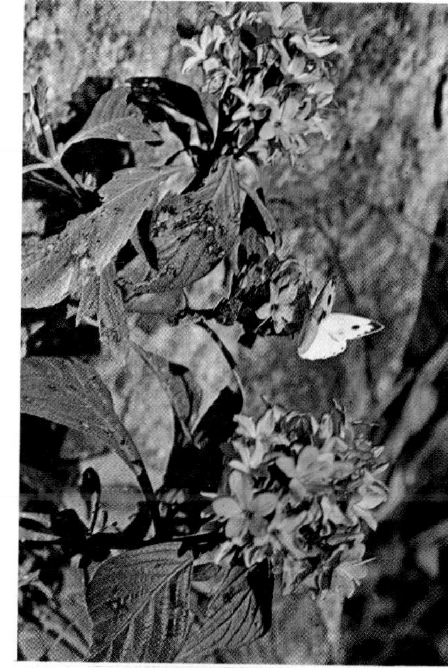

(b) *Acanihaceae* Blue Indian Acanthus

ssaenda macrophylla – "Dhobini"

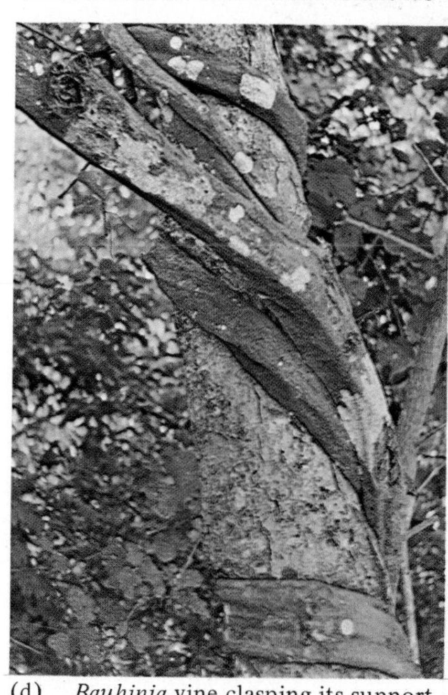

(d) *Bauhinia* vine clasping its support

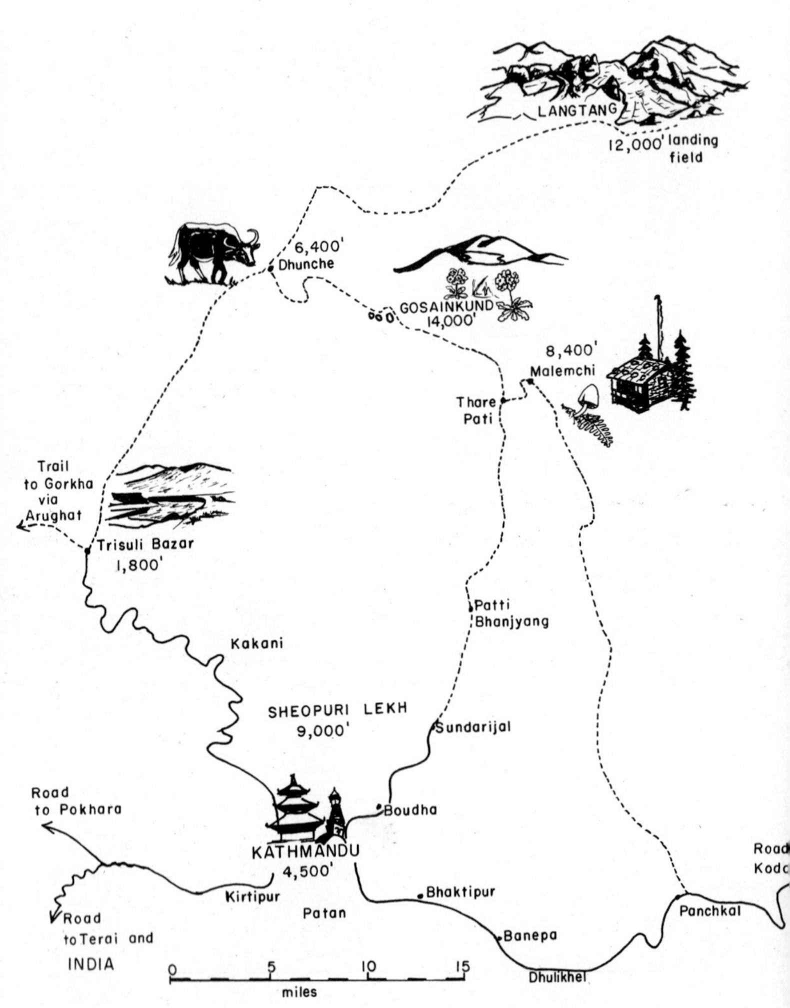
LANGTANG
12,000' landing field
6,400'
Dhunche
GOSAINKUND
14,000'
8,400'
Malemchi
Thare Pati
Trail to Gorkha via Arughat
Trisuli Bazar
1,800'
Patti Bhanjyang
Kakani
SHEOPURI LEKH
9,000'
Sundarijal
Road to Pokhara
Boudha
KATHMANDU
4,500'
Kirtipur
Patan
Bhaktipur
Panchkal
Banepa
Dhulikhel
Road to Terai and INDIA
0
5
10
15
miles

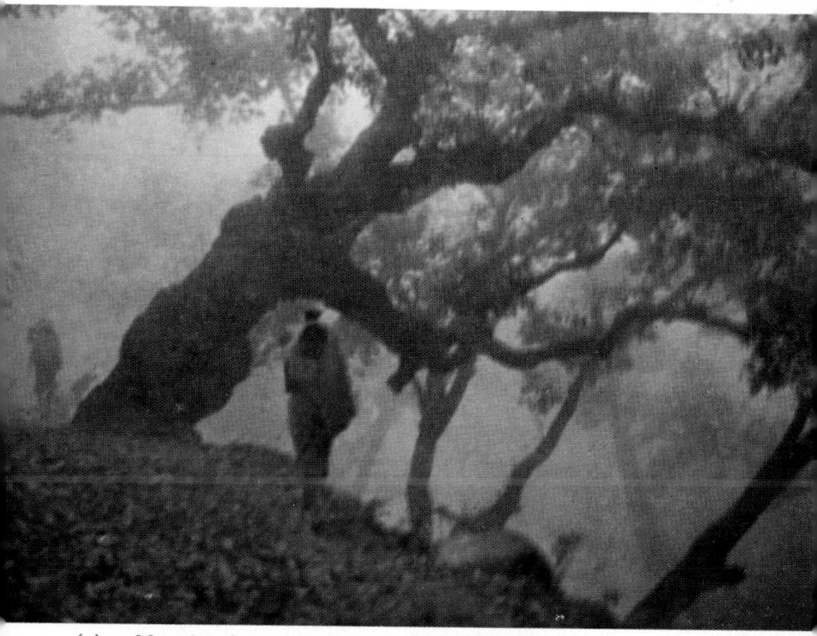

(a) Morning fog on trail to Kathmandu (oak forest)

ℛhododendron blooms on Shivapuri

(c) Hemlock-Rhododendron forest

(a) *Polygonum* flowers on trail above valley.

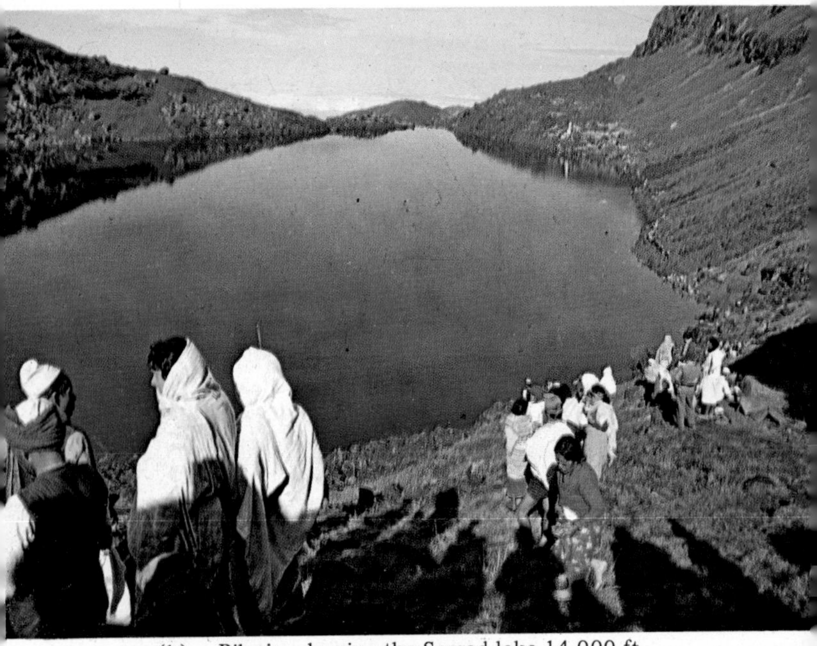

(b) Pilgrims leaving the Sacred lake 14,000 ft.

(d) Yellow Balsam

A VARIETY OF MOUNTAIN FLOWERS

(a) *Cyananthus lobatus*

(b) *Halenia elliptica*

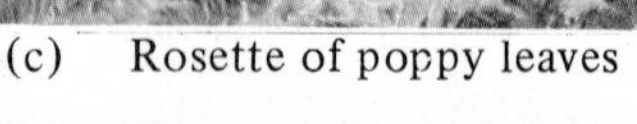

(c) Rosette of poppy leaves

(d) Yellow Poppy *Meconopsis*

(e) Cyananthus (Campanula Family)

(f) *Aguilegia* Columbine

Dogwood *Cornus capitata*

(b) Buttercup *Ranunculus*

) Blue Poppy *Meconopsis*

(d) Yellow Saxifrage *Saxifraga diversifolia*

inquefoil or "Bajra Danti" *Potentilla*

(f) *Agrimonia* with *Potentilla*

(a) "Kumkum Dhup" *Diaymocarpus*

(b) Another *Didymocarpus*

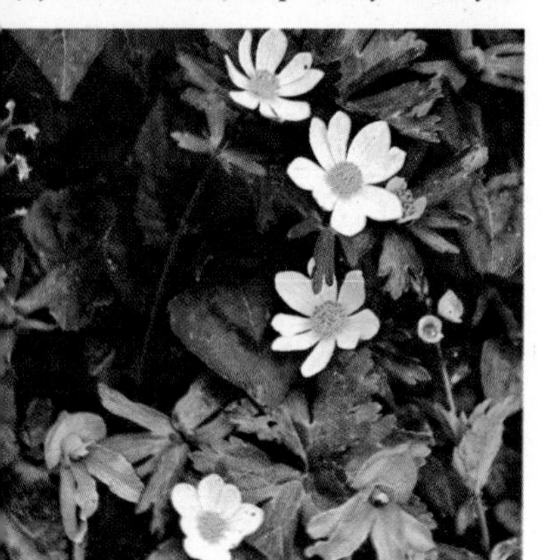

(c) White anemone & ground orchid

(d) Yellow Violets

(e) Pink *Pedicularis* and Orchid

(f) Red *Pedicularis*

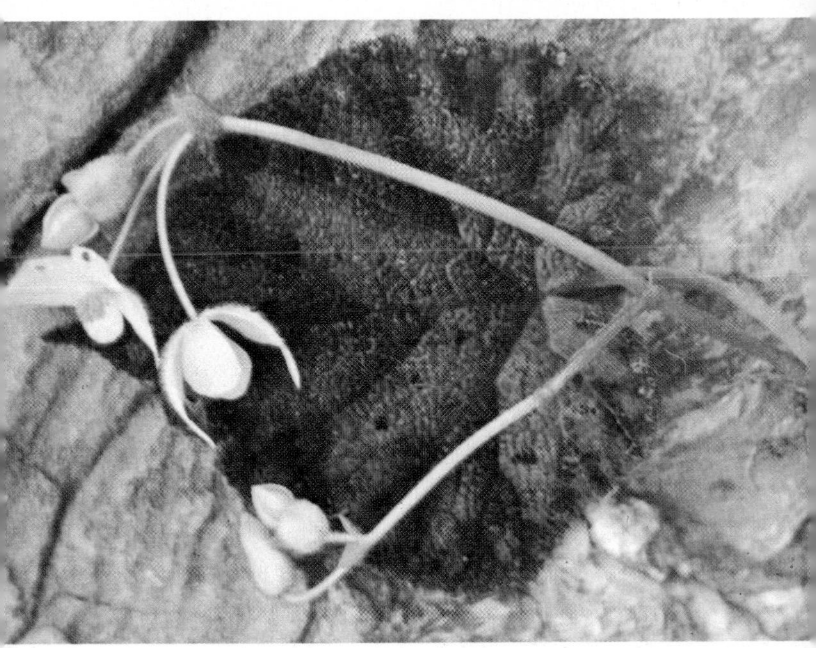

(a) Sherpa with red poppies

(b) *Dicentra scandens* and *Barleri*

(c) *Argemone mexicana* "Prickly Poppy"

(d) *Strobilanthus*

(a) *Hippophae* in upper Kali Gandaki

Incarvillea arguta "Pink Bignonia"

(c) *Hippophae* – lower Langtang

August Is Mushroom Season At Malemche

(a) Malemchi Village

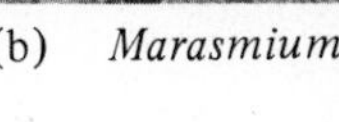

(b) *Marasmium*

(c) *Amanita* sp.

(d) *Cantharellus* sp.

(e) *Rusula* sp.

(a) *Amanita* sp.

(b) *Boletus* sp.

Edible mushrooms for sale

(d) *Aleuria aurantiaca* with *Ardisia* berries

Red Polypores and flower petals

(f) Sticky type from Bhutan

(a) *Dacromyces palmata*

(b) *Amanita* sp.

(c) A woody Polypore

(d) *Schizophyllum* sp.

(e) *Russula* sp.

(f) *Boletus* sp.

Morels with Jack-in-the-pulpit

Thangboche Monastery in different moods

Khumjung and Kunde seen from Thangboche

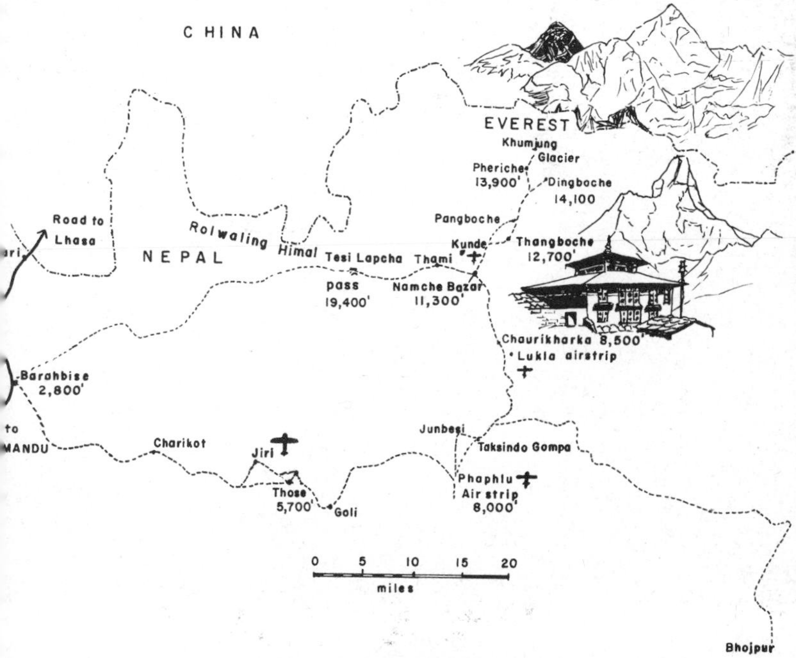

CHINA
EVEREST
Khumjung
Glacier
Pheriche
13,900'
Dingboche
14,100
Road to
Lhasa
Pangboche
Rolwaling Himal
NEPAL
Kunde
Thangboche
12,700'
Tesi Lapcha
pass
19,400'
Thami
Namche Bazar
11,300'
Chaurikharka 8,500'
Lukla airstrip
Barahbise
2,800'
to
MANDU
Charikot
Jiri
Junbesi
Taksindo Gompa
Phaphlu
Air strip
8,000'
Those
5,700'
Goli
0 5 10 15 20
miles
Bhojpur

(a) Alpine meadow near Khumbu Glacier 17,000 ft.

(b) Strange "mushrooms" of ice and rocks on Khumbu glacier

(a) Lichens and Edelweiss at 18,000 ft., Everest Area

(b) Gorakshep – dried plants in old lake bed 18,000 ft.

(a) *Ephedra gerardiana* in Everest area

(b) *Ephedra* in Langtang Valley 14,000 ft.

(a) Edelweiss (*Leontopodium*) above 12,000 ft.

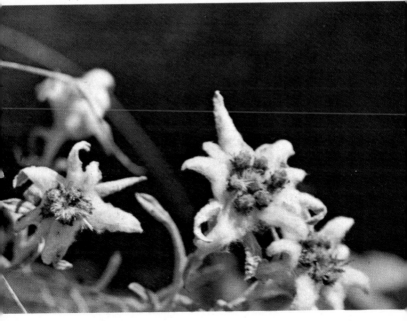

(b) Another Edelweiss from Langtang – 13,000 ft.

Gentians delight the Autumn visitor

(a) *Gentiana amoena* in Langtang Valley

(b) *Gentiana amoena*

(c) *Primula* leaves turn red in Autu

Two Peas or Legumes of the Mountain Regions

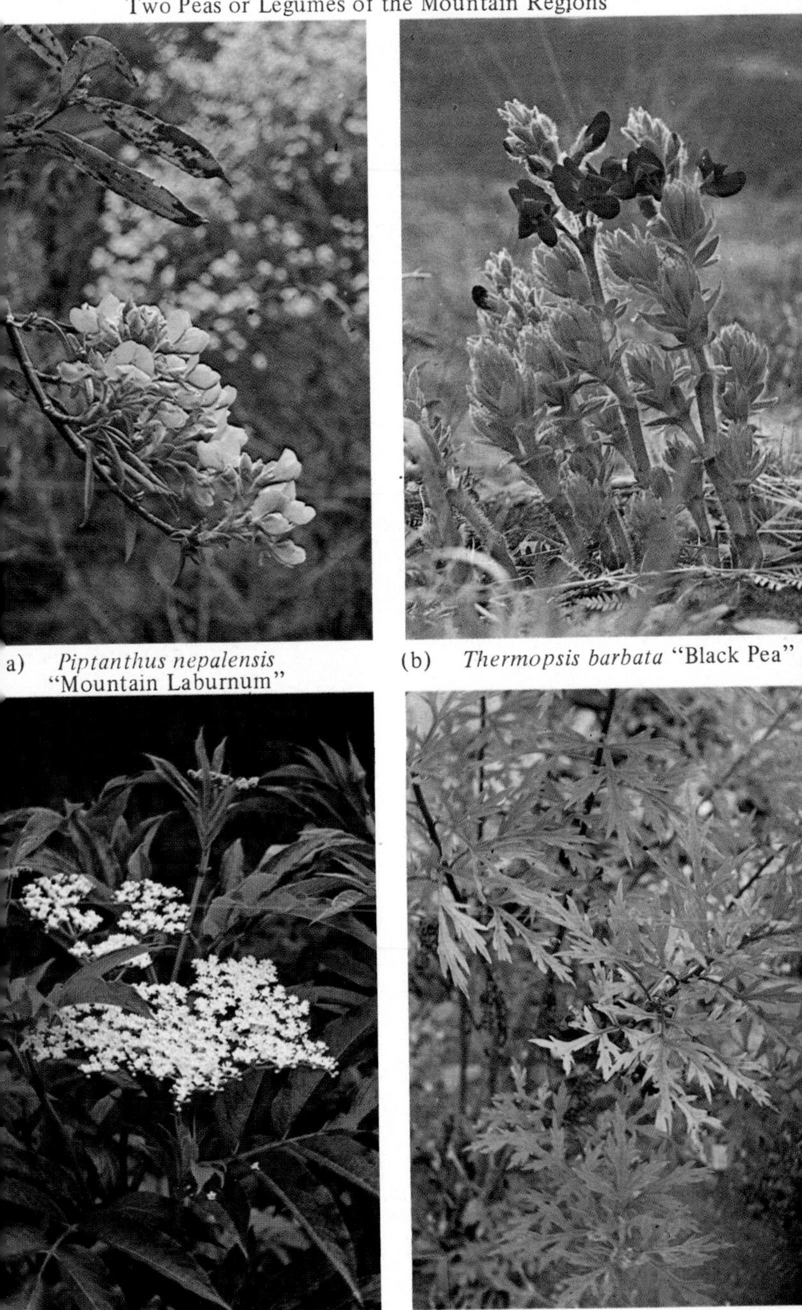

a) *Piptanthus nepalensis* "Mountain Laburnum"

(b) *Thermopsis barbata* "Black Pea"

:) *Sambucus* "Elderberry"

(d) *Artimesia* "Sage"

(b) *Lilium wallichianum* near Panchkhal

Coniferous Forest at Phaphlu 8,000 ft.

Hemlocks may attain a great size

Hemlock cones – *Tsuga dumosa*

(a) Deciduous forest of east Nepal with Magnolia blooming

) Details of *Magnolia campbellii*

Magnolia flowers "Champ"

(d) Magnolia tree in full bloom

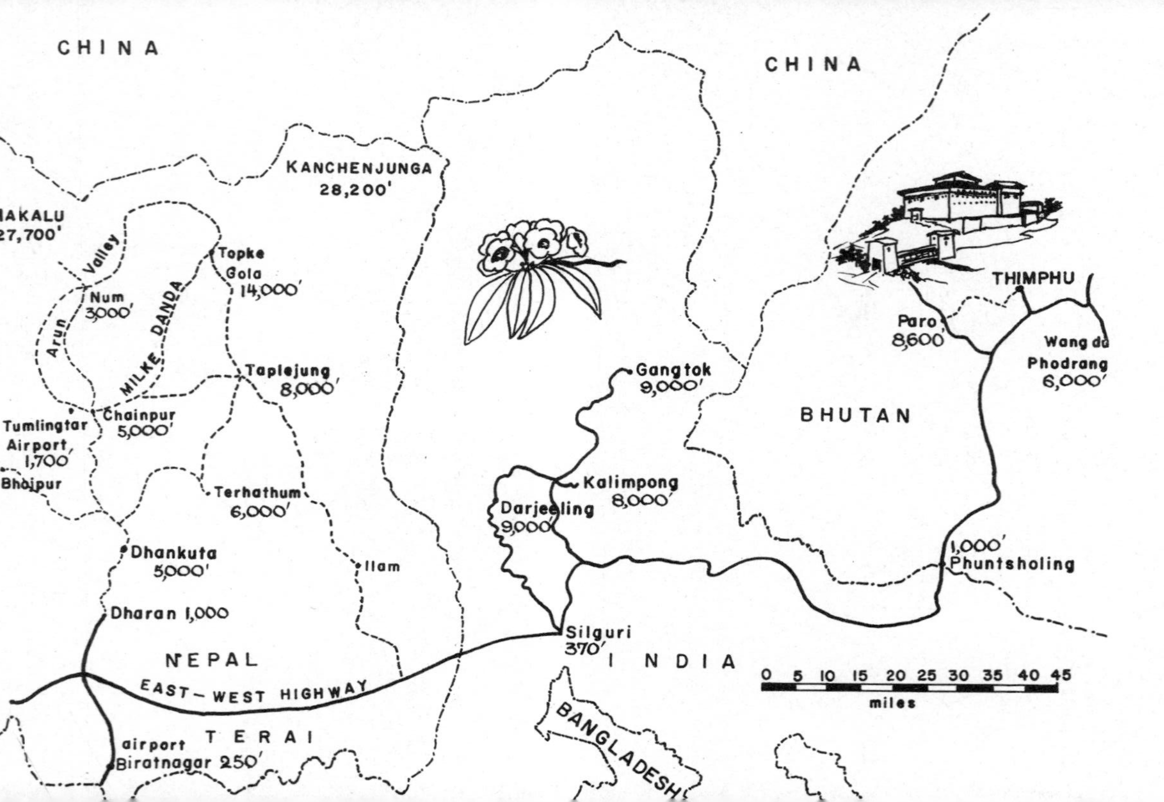

CHINA
CHINA
KANCHENJUNGA
28,200'
MAKALU
27,700'
Valley
Topke
Gola
14,000'
Num
3000'
Arun
MILKE DANDA
Taplejung
8,000'
Tumlingtar
Airport,
1,700
Bhojpur
Chainpur
5,000'
Terhathum
6,000'
Dhankuta
5000'
Ilam
Dharan 1,000
NEPAL
EAST-WEST HIGHWAY
TERAI
airport
Biratnagar 250'
Gangtok
9,000'
Kalimpong
8,000'
Darjeeling
9,000
Silguri
370'
INDIA
BANGLADESH
THIMPHU
Paro
8,600'
Wang du
Phodrang
6,000'
BHUTAN
1,000'
Phuntsholing
0 5 10 15 20 25 30 35 40 45
miles

(a) Heavily loaded porters reach the outskirts of Dhankuta

(b) Barbet with cricket

(c) Praying Mantis on flower

Tiger's Nest near Paro, Bhutan

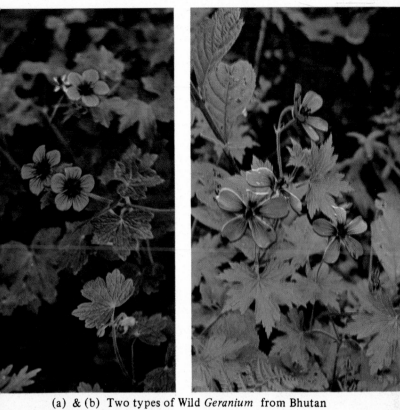

(a) & (b) Two types of Wild *Geranium* from Bhutan

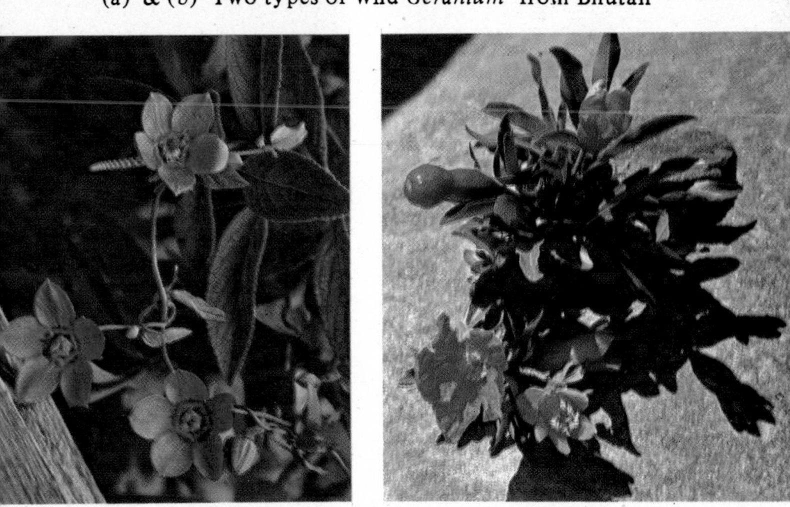

lue flowering vine by Tiger's Nest (d) Pomegranite "Darim" *Punica granatum*

(a) details of (b) Flowers and seeds

(b) *Lagerstroemia parviflora* "Crepe M

(c) Cultivated Crepe Myrtle *L. indica*

(d) *Duabanga grandiflora* "Lam

(a) *Costus speciosus* White Ginger

(b) *Curcuma* flowers

(c) *Hedychium ellipticum* "Kyamana"

(a) *Holarrhena antidysenterica*

(b) *Pandanus furcatus*
"Screw Pine" 'Kevada"

(c) Jasmin flowers

(d) Screw Pine fruit with Jasmin

(a) Arun Valley man with fruiting *Clerodendron*

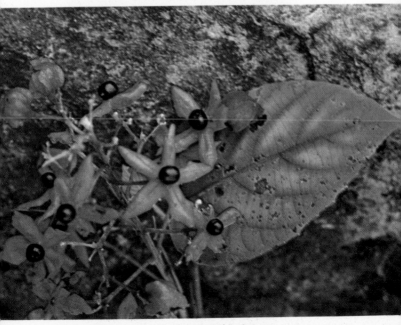

(b) More details of *Clerodendron* berries

(a) Alder woods (*Alnus nepalensis*)

(b) Waxy pink flowers

(c) "Jamun" tree in Pokhara
Eugenia jambos

(d) *Aeschynanthus* grows on trees

(e) *Cupressus torulosa* "Cypress t

The twisted vines of Num bridge have now been replaced

(a) Larch and Fir above Paro, Bhutan

(b) Juniper *J. recurva*

(c) Langtang Larch is different from the Bhutan one

(a) Old fir trees on Milke Danda ridge in East Nepal

Fir cones stand upright

(c) Great Hemlock trees on Punaka Pass

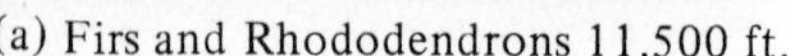

(a) Firs and Rhododendrons 11,500 ft.

(b) New leaves on Rhododendr

(c) *Rhododendron campanulatum* on Milk Danda

(a) Variety of Rhododendrons found in early May on Milke Danda

(b) Park-like setting of Rhododendrons and Firs on Milke Danda

(a) *Rhododendron thomsonii* at 12,000 ft.

(b) *Rh. cinnabarinum* with its associates

(c) *Rh. hodgsonii* & yellow *Rh. campylocarpum*

(a) *Rhododendron campanulatum* flowers

arboreum with Swallowtail butterfly

(c) *Pieris formosa*

(a) *Rhododendron campylocarpum*

(b) *Rh. cinnabarinum*

(c) *Rh. campanulatum*

(d) *Rhododendron lepidotu*
(two forms)

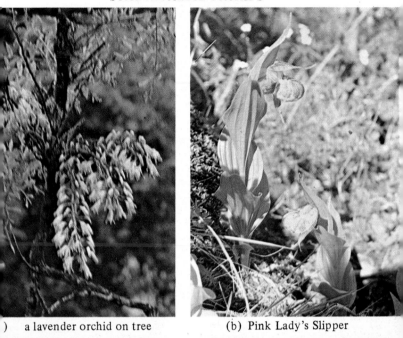

) a lavender orchid on tree

(b) Pink Lady's Slipper

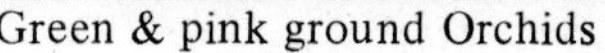

Green & pink ground Orchids

(d) Everlasting with pink ground orchid

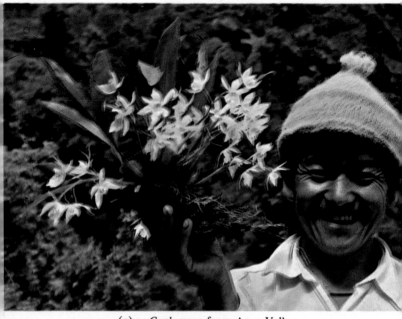

(a) *Coelogyne* from Arun Valley

(b) *Coelogyne* Pokhara valley

(a) details of *Coelogyne cristata* flower

(b) *Coelogyne* growing on rocks, Pokhara valley

(a) Flowers of *Dendrobium nobile*

(b) *Dendrobium nobile* on tree

(c) *Pleone humilis* on tree

SOME FERNS

(a) *Thelypteris* sp.

(b) *Nephrolepis tuberosa* "Panisar

(c) *Drynaria* sp. "Nest fern"

(d) *Cythea spinulosa* "Tree Fern"

(a) *Dicranopteris linearis*

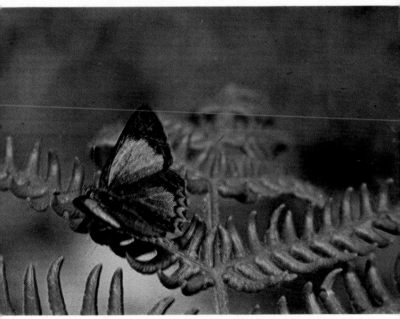

(b) *Woodwardia unigemmata* with butterfly

"Rasgari" – an orchid-like purple ginger *Roscoea purpurea*

growing above Helambu in August.

NOTES

Page

34 INTRODUCED PLANTS IN NEPAL

Although Nepal has abundant species of native flowering plants (6,500 species) it also has an old history of introducing exotic ones. Some are now closely linked with Nepalese tradition and culture.

a Poinsettias (*Euphorbia pulcherrima*) taller than people are famous in Pokhara Valley. This exotic from Mexico got access to Nepal through the Gurkha soldiers and is now very popular and common in Nepal with the name "Lal Pate"

b The exotic Bottlebrush tree (*Callistemon linearis*) came from Australia. Here it frames a statue of Jung Bahadur Rana, an enthusiastic discoverer of exotic things from Victorian England. The Rana Prime Ministers became ardent gardeners.

c *Plumeria acuminata* "Choya Phul" by Arun Valley village in East Nepal. An exotic from Mexico, most admired for its fragrant flowers.

35 Bougainvillea – A native of Brazil adorns garden walls and
a trees with its brilliantly colored flower bracts. The real flowers are small.

b Silky oak (*Grevillea robusta*) Au Australian tree with huge dimentions grown as an avenue tree along roads. Nepalese call it "Kangio Phul" or comb flower refering to the arrangement of flowers.

c Wisteria - A Chinese shrub with climbing habit, commonly grown along walls and on tall wooden supports or trellises.

d Prickly Pear (*Opuntia* sp.) An American cactus naturalized in Nepal along gorges of big rivers and on slopes of hot and humid valleys. Its local name "Hati Kane" refers to the fleshy flat leaf-like stems which look like elephant ears. It is oten grown with the small Crown-of-thorns (*Euphorbia splendens*) on walls and along field edges to keep out men and animals.

36 Many beautiful flowering plants of the Himalayas have become familiar to people around the world as Garden Flowers.

a & b *Rhododendron arboreum* – "Lali Guras" is the National

Flower of Nepal. It grows as a tree to a height of 20 or 30 ft. It flowers in March and April and may come in scarlet, pink or white. The different colors are associated with altitudinal variation. Generally only the scarlet are found from 4,000′ to 8,000 ft. but in the upper range and above, various shades of pink and the white may be found.

c *Iris kumaonensis* flowers in May at 11,000 ft. in western Nepal. A group selected to show the wide color variation has been placed in a nearby Juniper. Other Iris species growing at lower altitudes have longer stems and may appear even more like our many garden hybrids.

37 *Primula denticulat a*at 10,000 ft. showing colour variations.

a Many of the Primulas have been introduced to gardens.

b *Lilium nepalense* "Ban Lasun" is one of the giant lilies eagerly sought after by plant hunters for western gardens.

c *Dendrobium densiflorum* "Sun Gava" is a popular orchid from central and eastern Himalaya between 2 000 and 4,000 ft.

38 Along walls and fences near the villages we find various useful and interesting plants.

a *Jatropa curcas* "Sajiwan" – a hedge plant of hot valleys which exudes a soapy liquid when injured. Children blow "soap" bubbles with it. The seeds contain a high amount of fixed oil useful for smearing and in lubricating.

b *Oroxylum indicum* "Tatelo" – A small tree of 20–25 ft. The seeds in the long pods have silvery paper around them and so are very decorative for garlands etc.It has religious as well as medicinal value.

c *Adhatoda vasica* "Asuro" – A wayside shrub commonly grown as hedge. Leaves are medicinal for the remedy of cough and fever.

39 Whether high or low, the grass family is important to man and beast.

a Yaks grazing at 16,000 ft. near Ringmo in western Nepal.

b An elephant amongst a jungle of elephant grasses in Chitaun at 600 ft. (*Saccharum* sp., *Imperata* sp., *Phragmitis* sp)

40 Tamang-Sherpa people grow millet (*Elusine coracana* and "Junelo" (*Sorghum vulgare*) in unirrigated fields in the upper Trisuli and Langtang Valley to 12,000 ft. The rain shadow in Langtang makes it possible to extend crops beyond the usual limit of agriculture in Nepal at about 8,000–9,000 ft.

41 Most of our cereal grains have been developed from wild

grasses.

a *Themeda* sp. is one of the common grasses on lowland hills, and, being very tall, is often used for thatching.

b Broom Grass or "Kucho" from which brooms are made comes from the flowering stems of *Thysanolaena maxima.*

c Wheat field being protected by fence of barberry (*Berberis asiatica*). Barberry and wheat are alternate hosts for the black rust (*Puccinia graminis*) that destroys a considerable amount of the wheat crop each year.

d Rice-- Paddy or "Dhan" (*Oriza sativa*) is the principle crop of Nepal below 7,000 ft.

e Pink and white buckwheat flowers (*Fagopyrum esculentum*) growing with yellow "Sesame" flowers (*Guizotia abyssinica*) The seeds of the seasame are used for oil as well as eaten for their nutty flavor.

f Millet and Amaranthus are important corps for mountain dwellers all along the Himalayas. This scene is in Bhutan.

42 MIDLAND FORESTS HAVE GIVEN WAY TO FARMS
The sub-tropical and temperate broad-leaved forests of the
43 world have become the chief settlement areas for people, since the soil is generally fertile for crops. The hilly midlands of Nepal are generally terraced. Fertile fields and terraced hills in the middle altitudes. (2,000–8,000ft.) can be very beautiful as well as productive as seen from Kashmir and Nepal to Bhutan and Assam

44 AGRICULTURAI ACTIVITIES

a With irrigation it is possible to grow three crops a year in the fertile soil of the old lake bed of Kathmandu Valley. Wheat is harvested in late May and the paddy rice is golden by late September. Vegetables or a "harvest" of bricks may then come from the thick clay of the fields.

b Six-rowed Tibetan barley "wah" is one of the principle crops in the higher Himalayan region. Upstream valley winds are used for winnowing the grain in early summer. Then it is popped and ground into "tsampa".

45 Heavy bags of maize, millet or wheat are carried down to the
a grinding mills which are generally located on a stream.

b A small stream of water diverted from the main stream provides power for turning the mill wheels.

c An ingenious device permits the grain to trickle slowly from the basket into the hole in the turning grindstone. Flour comes out on the sides after the grain has been crushed by the stones.

46 The destruction of forests in the middle latitudes may be slow and almost un-noticed or rapid and dramatic.

a Cattle, buffalo and goats may be beneficial when they graze in small numbers in the forests. If the number of grazing animals becomes too large, young tree shoots are destroyed and the forest can no longer reproduce itself. It may remain an attractive grove of aging shade trees which gradually die and are not replaced.

b Pioneer settlers clear areas of forest land to grow crops. The surrounding forest provides them with fuel and lumber as long as the number of settlers remains small and the fields are kept fertile with sufficient animal manures.

c Fodder is cut from tall trees in sub-tropical broadleaf forests instead of using valuable field space for raising hay.

d Tree leaves make good fodder and are carried to the animals when they are kept tied, to prevent destruction to the fields with growing crops. Too much population pressure and demand for leafy braches means severe cutting of tree branches and young shoots until the forests gradually disappear and the last remaining trees look more like poles.

47 Slash-burn agriculture is found throughout the less populated tropical and sub-tropical regions of the world. Forests are destroyed to get two or three years of crops. New areas of forest are burned and cleared each year and older areas which have lost their fertility are abandoned. It is a type of pioneer migratory agriculture which is only possible when land with forests is plentiful. Steep slopes which have lost their trees may also rapidly lose their soil through rapid erosion and never recover enough to produce either crops or forests unless special measures are taken.

48 Grass and its tree relative, bamboo are important materials for constructing roofs in many places where the tall grasses grow. Generally the thatch must be renewed every three years.

49 Sugar canes are grown in the Terai and in subtropical valleys.

50 The squash family provides food in many forms– green shoots, flowers, fruits and wild forms Here are some cucumbers:

a Tharus dry cucumber slices for future use.

b The male flowers of pumpkin and other members of the squash family are dipped in batter and fried as a vegetable.

c Wild cucumbers are bitter and called "kukur kankro" (dog cucumber)

d Some cucumbers grow very large and many be stored under roof eaves for future use. These were in a hill village above Pokhara.

51a As in Italy, villages are often built on the hilltops. It is not only a strategic location but is more healthy since malaria has been a problem of the lowlands in the past.

b Amaranthus crop stands in front of massive rammed-earth farm houses in western Bhutan. High winds make it desirable to keep an air space between the roof and the house and stones on the roof. Most people live in rain -shadow valleys at about 8,000 ft. where the forests are largely pine.

52 THE POTATO FAMILY (*Solanaceae*)

53 Most of the edible members of the family have been introduced from the Americas; potatos, tomatos, and red peppers. This interesting family also contains some important medicinal plants and drugs which can be quite poisonous; datura, belladona, kantakari and tobacco. The berries are sometimes enclosed in attractive papery covers like small ornamental lanterns. (d)

54 FIBER PLANTS USEFUL FOR WEAVING

a Marijuana or Hemp (*Cannabis sativa*) has become too well known for its drug properties. It also is the source for a useful strong fiber and its seeds are commonly crushed to make a cooking oil which can be used without any drug effects. It is a very common weed throughout the world.

b&c Two kinds of Nettles found in the Himalayas.
Urtica dioca or the common nettle "Sisnu" has a very painful sting when touched, from the many glandular hairs. A common punishment is to beat the culprit with nettles. In spite of this feature nettles are used for their food value – new leaves cooked like spinach. The fibers are woven into strong cloth.

55 The Mustard Family (*Cruciferae*) besides giving us many lovely wild flowers and valued garden flowers, has provided us with some of our most common vegetables and a cooking oil. Most villages have a mustard oil press where the local people can prepare this main cooking oil used in the midlands. Cabbages, cauliflowers, kohlrabi and radishes are favorite

vegetables in Nepal and may attain a very large size.

56 The Northwestern region of Nepal (Jumla, Humla & Dolpa) is drier than the central and the eastern regions. The landscape is open and undulating. Lofty valleys are suitable for raising cattle, sheep and horses.

57a Dryness of the region is reflected in the type of houses which have flat roofs.

b Lake Rara lies at 9,808 ft. altitude and is set in a saucer of pine clad hills with a few relicts of *Rhododendron arboreum.*

c *Menyanthes trifòliata* "Bog Bean" growing in water of inlet to Lake Rara at 9,808 ft. altitude. It was known to grow in Kashmir and this record extends its range in the Himalayas.

58 NW Nepal has much to share with the forest flora of Kumaon, Kashmir and Afghanistan farther west.

a The magnificent Himalayan Cedar (*Cedrus deodara*) reaches its geographical limit of distribution in the western half of

b Nepal, and so does the west Himalayan Spruce, (*Picea Smithiana*) Villagers in the Jumla area protect Deodar as

c sacred trees. Such trees are often gigantic, measuring 140 ft. tall.

59a Natural timber-line (12,000 to 14,000 ft) in the Himalayas is almost always marked by the presence of the white Birch (*Betula utilis.*)

b Lake Phoksumdo lies at 11,700 ft. and represents a drowned valley. Its blue-green waters give it great charm.

c *Buddleia tibetica* var. *grandiflora* is an element of Tibetan flora which extends to the transhimalayan region of Nepal such as Dolpa and Mustang.

60 The coniferious forests of Kanjiroba Himal consist mainly of Blue Pine (*Pinus wallichiana*) and West Himalayan Spruce. (*Picea Smithiana*).

61a Poplar (*Populus ciliata*) is a common component of the deciduous forest of western Nepal. This species is absent from central Nepal to Sikkim but reappears in Bhutan and Southeast Tibet

b The mixed forest consists of walnut (*Juglans regia*) Maples, (*Acer* sp.), Horse chestnut, (*Aesculus indica*) Poplar (*Populus ciliata*) and some coniferous trees like (*Picea smithiana*)

c Mixed temperate forests have colorful floors including bright colored maple seedlings.

d Forest edges have fragrant Daphne and colorful primulas.

62a *Daphne bholua* "kagat Pata" is an evergreen shrub of 2–3 ft.

tail and is the principle source of paper pulp for Nepalese paper. It grows all along the temperate region of Nepal at 5,000– 8,000 ft. Flowers are fragrant.

b *Daphne bholua* var *glacialis* is a deciduous variety occuring at higher elevations 9–11 000 ft. Also with fragrant flowers.

c& *Stellara chamaejasme* also belongs to the Daphne family
d (Thymelaeaceae). It occurs in profusion in drier regions of NW Nepal at about 11 to 14,000 ft. in many colors. It colonizes abandoned fields and terraces along river banks. Flowers are very fragrant

63a *Leptodermis* belongs to Rubiaceae and many species are involved in the Himalayas. A systematic study on them still remains to be done. Species of *Leptodermis* have pretty flowers with a range of color from white to purple and pink. The shrubs are small in stature and occur mostly in open places along trails and forest edges.

b *Jasminum humile* occurs on forest edges. This pretty shrub has a wide range of distribution all along the Himalayas from 6 000 to 11,500 ft.

c *Viburnum erubescens* is a common shrub of temperate forests of mixed evergreen trees at 6,000 to 10,000 ft. The leaves have a peculiar smell when crushed.

d Bhutan has seven species of *Jasminum* and four of them have white flowers. This scandant jasmine is found along forest edges and along roads and trails. Very sweet scented.

64 Nepal is quite rich in Primroses. There are 67 species of *Primula* occuring in the alpine and Sub-alpine regions of Nepal. Ten species are endemic to the Nepal Himalaya.

a *Primula strumosa* (yellow) and *P. denticulata* appear early in the spring soon after the melting of snow.

b Most of the Primula in the section *petiolaris* are dwarf and flowers are sprayed loosely.

c *Androsace* is a near relative of *Primula* and occurs mostly in dry situations. This was in an area of pine forests.

d *Primula denticulata* is the most common of the *Primula* species found in Nepal. It occurs from 5,000 ft. to 10,000 ft. and blooms at almost any season.

e A field of yellow primroses (*P. strumosa*) can be a very beautiful sight in early June above timberline.

f This large white primrose (*P. obliqua*) was found blooming with a group of yellow primroses at about 13,000 ft. on Namum Pass above the Marysangdi Valley.

65 a Some members of the *Androsace* can be found at very high altitudes where they combat dryness by having very short stems and leaves reduced to round fleshy structures similar to the *Saxifraga*. Here is one that occurs as a large cusion of tiny plants around 16,000 ft above Mukut.

b There are numerous species involved in both *Androsace* and and in the *Saxifraga* genera This is one of the saxifraga.

c Brightly colored Androsace from the Goropani area.

d A cushion type Androsace.

e A succulent type from Phoksumdo Tal area.

f Primula from North of Pokhara.

66 *Clematis montana* is one of the commonest vines in montane Himalayas from 6,500 ft. to 9,000 ft. The flower size varies from place to place with smaller flowers in drier regions.

67a Detail of Mountain Clematis from near Rara Lake.

b Arun Valley of eastern Nepal is the most humid area in Nepal. The flora of this region is very rich and one finds many vines. Botanical identity is not yet certain for this vine.

c *Clematis acutangula* is a pretty vine of Sikkim and Bhutan. It extends into South Tibet but does not occur in Nepal.

68a When one goes from the Dolpo behind Dhaulagiri to the upper Kali Gandaki, or behind Annapurna, one must go by quite high passes. At 19,000 ft. on the top of Mulah Pass there is only snow and rocks but the views of Dhaulagiri II

b. and its surroundings are superb.

c The Tibetan Plateau on the Kali Gandaki side of the Mulah Pass at about 16,000 ft. flat and rolling with alpine cushion plants and water that freezes nightly.

69a Here is 26, 146 ft. Annapurna II as seen from the south from above Siklis. Avalanches are common occurances.

b This is the same peak as seen from the north near Pisang in the Marsyangdi Valley. Coniferous forests are in the northern valley. Oaks, Rhododendron and grassy meadows are more common on the southern slopes.

70 Landslide in the upper Kali Gandaki between Ghasa and Leyte. Since the Himalayas are young and still rising there are numerous landslides caused by loosely consolidated material and steep slopes- for which human activities are not to blame. The landscape is very fragile when the heavy monsoon rains come especially, so the consequences of overcutting, mining, overgrazing and road building are quickly

apparent also.

71 Small map to show some locations in one of the most popular trekking areas in Nepal. One can walk from the sub-tropics to coniferous forests and the semi-desert rain shadow region.

72a Rain Shadow Country – The upper Kali Gandaki lies on the north of the main Himalayan range and the Monsoon rains cannot penetrate there. The Kali Gandaki river cuts through the Himalayas between Dhaulagiri and Annapurna making a deep gorge of some 16,000 ft.

73a *Cargana brevispina* is an indicator of rain shadow country
b in Nepal. The flower buds of this plant from the pea family taste like fresh peas.

c *Rosa sericea* occurs as a common shrub on exposed places above 9,000 ft. It is a single rose of 4 petals and the branches are very bristly and thorny.

74a The alpine meadows of Tilicho Pass have made good grazing for yaks.

b The transitional zone between the humid regions on the south of the main Himalayan range and the arid north is characterized by the occurance of the Blue Pine (*Pinus wallichiana*).

75a *Lonicera spinosa* is very characteristic of the arid regions to the north of the Himalayas. The flowers are quite fragrant and its honey is much sought by tiny birds.

b *Oxygraphis* colours meadows as well as forest floors. It is one of the early flowers in the spring.

c *Caltha* is a relative of *Oxygraphis* but it occurs usually in wet marshy and boggy places. "Alpine buttercups

d Alpine *Astragulus* has very short stems
Blue prickly pea *Astragulus* is common around Marpha and Jomosum but disappears higher up and is replaced by the yellow and creamy forms.

f Creamy prickly pea *Caragana* from the Tilicho Lake trail where it can be found between about 10,000 and 12,000 ft. *Astragalus* and *Caragana* are abundant in drier regions of NW Nepal. Their pealike flowers are very attaractive to the traveller but they are not easy genera for the botanist to identify into species

76 Euphorbias exude milky sap when injured. Their flowers are showy due to colored leaves (bracts). Compositae flowers are grouped in a head. Marginal flowers have showy petals.

a *Euphorbia himalayensis* and *E. wallichii* are common on

b exposed slopes in temperate regions.

c *Senceio* sp. A wild shrubby composite often growing along forest edges. "Goldenrod"

d Sunflower growing in Paro, Bhutan. Its seeds are used as a source of oil.

77a *Ainsliaea pteropoda* (Sahadeva, Sahadevi) grows in oak forests. It is believed in hilly regions that this plant helps one to fall in love when offered to the opposite sex.

b This view shows how this tiny plant grows while (a) shows the details of a single flower which with three others makes up the composite flower head. Each has 5 petals connected in an irregular tube around the stamen and pistil.

c Here is a small composite which has gone to seed. The typical wind-bourne seeds are most familiar to us in the Dandylion

78 People of temperate regions are familiar with relatively small herbaceous members of the Composite family. In the tropics one can find composites growing as vines and almost small trees. This Marrue Sunflower was growing in Pokhara Valley.

79a The Naudanda ridge of Pokhara after deforestation gives ground to many grasses and herbs. Daisys bloom to color the ridge.

b Tree-like daisys and poinsettias grow around one of the government office buildings in Gantok, Sikkim.

80 Members of *Compositae* have a wide range of distribution and many of them are considered to be weeds since they grow well in cultivated fields. Here are a few temperate region types found in Nepal.

81 There are two pines in Nepal Himalayas. The Chir Pine (*Pinus roxburhgii*) is subtropical and usually occurs between 2,500 and 6,500 ft. It has 3 long needles and is the chief source of rosin and turpentine. The Blue pine (*Pinus wallichiana*) is a temperate species which is generally found between 6,000 and 11,000 ft. in the inner ranges of the Himalayas. It has 5 needles which are shorter than those of the Chir Pine.

82 The Rose Family (Rosaceae) consists of a wide range of Plants from a tiny strawberry plant to many of our fruit trees and bushes. Forest trees like the Beam and the giant *Stranvaesia* are also in this useful family.

a *Rosa sericea* – a shrub or 3–7 ft. which occurs on open

slopes and forest edges in the temperate hills at about 7 to 10,00ↄ ft.

b At times it is associated with *Cotoneaster* in drier southern aspects. *Cotoneaster* species often form prostrate cushions and are very attractive among rocks.

c Strawberries (*Frageria* sp.) grow on the forest floor in the temperate regions above 8,000 ft. Two species are found in the Nepal Himalayas (*F. daltoniana* & *F. nubicole*).

83 Peaches and apricots probably originated in Persia. They grow well in the dry regions of western Nepal and have been planted in the Transhimalayan regions with success.

84 "Machhapuchhare" shows its fish-tail as seen from the west. This 22,942 ft. peak is the "Matterhorn" of Nepal.

85 Three faces of Machhapuchhare, the Fish-tail peak. This much photographed peak shows many moods in its different aspects. Being closer to Pokhara, it seems to be higher than the Annapurnas which form a wall of mountains behind it.

86 Lying to the NW of Machhapuchhare and surrounded by high peaks of the Annapurna range is a 14,000 ft. glacial valley called Annapurna Sanctuary. A sometimes dangerous but beautiful trail has become a favorite trek from Pokhara.

87 The site of the Sanctuary can be seen from Pokhara. The peaks from left to right are: Annapurna South-23,683 ft., Hiunchuli–21,133 ft (in front of the Sanctuary), and Annapurna I–26,545 ft (forming north wall of Sanctuary). The shoulder of Machhapuchhare can be seen rising to the right foreground. Because these high mountains extend so far south in the Pokhara area, this region has about the heaviest rainfall in Nepal most years. (150")

88a Iris and Anemones are some of the first flowers to be seen after the melting of snow in the temperate zone.

b Less population pressure in Manang Valley behind the Annapurnas has meant that there are still luxuriant coniferous forests. Chame Village.

89 Two faces of Dhaulagiri. (26,795 ft.).

a The southern slopes of this great peak are wooded as the area is wet.

b On the northern side the area is arid and the slopes are bare.

90a *Thunbergia coccinea* vine bears bunches of flowers in autumn. This was in the woods above Pokhara but it is also frequently seen in the forests around Kathmandu Valley.

b *Luculia gratissima* of the Cinchona Family is one of the prettiest shrubs to be seen in the autumn woods of Kathmandu and Pokhara areas. Sometimes they bloom on cliff faces.

91 Flowering shrubs and trees of the sub-tropical forests.

b This *Dobinea vulgaris* of the ash Family was blooming in the autumn at the same place as the *Thunbergia* and *Luculia.* They usually are found on exposed slopes and along forest fringes.

d e "Chilaune" *Schima wallichii* and Chestnut *Castanopsis indica*
& f form the dominant vegetation in Subtropical Nepal east of the Kali Gandaki "Chilaune" is in the Tea Family and the flowers resemble tea flowers. The closeup picture shows the young red leaves as well as the nut-like seed pods.

c e *Osbeckia* species grow as small shrubs on the forest fringes.
& a The flowers are quite attractive and showy when they bloom in the summer. Their leaves may also take on bright red and yellow colors as they get old. These were blooming at the same time as the "Chilauni" in Arun Valley in May.

92 "Bhusure" (*Leucosceptrum canum*) is the only tree member of
a b the Mint Family (*Labiatae*) in Nepal. Flowering spikes resemble Bottle brush but they stand erect, unlike the hanging spikes of the latter. This is a tree of the Pokhara Region (7,000 ft.) and humid east Nepal.

93a *Buddleia asiatica* "Bhimsenpate" is commonly grown as a village shrub. Its leaves and flowers are widely used for religious purposes. The small black, white and yellow moth is usually found around the sweet-smelling flowers in the spring.

b "Nilo Bhusure" (*Caryopteris* sp.) is in the *Verbenaceae* Family. It grows on open slopes and along forest clearings around 5–7,000 ft.

94 Berries are pretty but not always good to eat–

a "Asuro" (*Dicroa febrifuga*) has blue berries which are not eaten. The roots and leaves are used as an emetic and to bring down fevers. These were growing near the Gurung village of Khilang at 5,000 ft. This is a common shrub of open ravines and bare hills.

b *Smilax* sp. bears beautiful berries on its climbing branches. Its leaves do not look like those of other monocotyledonous plants (grasses, corns, bamboos) but resembles dicotlyle donous leaves as the ones on the front in the picture.

c "Satuwa" (*Paris polyphylla*) is a well known medicinal plant of Nepal. Rhizomes are anthielmintic. The long threads represent petals for this strange lily. It occurs in the forest floor of the upper temperate region between about 5,500 ft. and 9,000 ft.

d *Paris* bears beautiful berries in the fall which are not eaten.

95a "Bilouni" (*Maesa chisea*) bears watery berries. The roots, bark and leaves are insecticidal. Local people also use it for fish poisoning. It grows in sub-tropical and temperate regions often near streams.

b "Birbanka" (*Arisaema tortuosum*) is one of the most common "Jack in the pulpits" in temperate Nepal. The bright seeds are given with salt to sheep for colic. The roots may be used to kill worms in cattle.

c There are over 100 species of *Arisaema* distributed mainly in Asia although several occur in tropical Africa and eastern North America and Mexico. Here is a group to show the variety found in temperate Kali Gandaki valley in June. The ones at far left and right are *Arisaema costatum*. The center plant with many leafflets is *Arisaema consanguineum*. The one beside it needs identification.

96a *Arisaema tortuosum* stands erect like an aggresive serpent with a long tongue sticking out. It bears red berries (also see p. 95 b.). The Nepali name for the fruiting heads of several of the Arisaemas is Sarpa Makai or Serpent's Corn.

b *Remusatia vivipara* often growns on tree trunks. The showy spathe reflects back exposing the flowers on the spadix.

c *Arisaema griffithii* looks terrific due to its extended spathe that resembles the hood of an angry King Cobra. These were found in the temperate woods on the way to Annapurna Sanctuary in late May. Near Gandrung they were being picked for pickling. Here is front, back, and side views.

d The trailing 15 inch spathe and erect appendix were quite interesting in this aroid seen above Leyte at about 8,000 ft. in June.

97a Monkshood (*Aconitum spicatum*) The famous "Bikh" (means poison) of Nepal is well known as an item of export as a crude drug. The tubers are deadly poisonous and are also used to poison the hunting spikes to kill Musk Deer in the Jumla area. It occurs in the sub-alpine region.

b The Gentain Vine (*Tripterosperumum volubile* or *Gentiana speciosa*) was seen along the forest trails between Ghandrung and Goropani Pass at around 9,000 ft. in late May.

98a Khasru oak (*Quercus semecarpifolia*) forms extensive forests all along the upper temperate region of the Himalayas. It sheds its leaves in areas of heavy snow. In this picture the trees are laden with *usnea* lichen.
Mature leaves of "Khasru" are brittle and do not have the spiny margins found on young leaves. Younger leaves are used as fodder for cows and buffalos.

c "Dhalne Katus" (*Castanopsis indica*) is the most common of the wild chestnuts of the sub-tropical zone of the eastern Himalayas. It is commonly found in association with Chilauni (*Schima wallichii*) (also see p. 91.)

d "Bansi" (*Quercus lamellosa*) These tall oaks bear very interesting acorns. Their long leaves resemble those of the chestnut. Groups of trees are often found in upper subtropical forests of the eastern Himalayas.

99 "Lekh Pipal" (*Populus ciliata*). This Poplar is the only tree species found in the upper Kali Gandaki near Muktinath and Jomsom. It has become an important species for the afforestation of Transhimalayan Nepal.

a View from Muktinath toward Dhaulagiri Himal.

c Leaves and Catkins near Marpha. The seeds are covered with "cotton".

b Horse Chestnut (*Aesculus indica*) is an important tree of the deciduous forests of western Nepal. It does not occur naturally in the eastern part of Nepal.

100a Barberry (*Berberis asiatica*) "Chutro" is a common wayside shrub along trails and fences in midland hills. The dark blue berries have a refreshing sweet and sour taste. It causes diarrhea if taken in quantities.

b *Mahonia napaulenisis* "Jamane mandro" is in the same family as the Barberry and bears similar flowers and fruits. This shrub grows more like a small tree 5 to 10 ft. tall. The wood has a bright yellow color. A beautiful crown of holly like compound leaves grows on the top of each branch and the flowers appear in early spring.

c *Berberis aristata* also known as "Chutro" is a shrub of warm temperate hills from 6,000 to 9,000 ft. Its fruit is also eaten by local people. The roots and bark are medicinal and used for various skin diseases.

d Barberry plants get beautiful colors in their drying leaves in the fall. These were seen in the area around Khumjung in the Everest area. Not many plants in the Himalayas change the color of their leaves in the fall. Sometimes in the monsoon tropics tree leaves change color and fall off in the spring just before monsoon rains bring new leaves.

101a Some Himalayan flowers are exceptionally tiny. A snapdragon, Saxifrage, Geranium and pea (*Parochaetus*) with flowers as small as a thumbnail.

b The pea flower of Parochaetus matches its color with the Fairy Gentians.

c *Hemiphragma heterophylla* with its pink flowers and red fruitings trails its runners through a group of Fairy Gentians.

d A small single Delphinium growing in western Bhutan.

e Tiny flowers of *Corydalis cashmiriana* are one of the early signs of spring in the sub-alpine region at 10,000 ft.

f Tiny flowers cast their shadows on a birch bark background.

102a "Simal" or Silk Cotton (*Salmalia malabaricum*) bears very attractive flowers when the tree is leafless in March.

b Many birds are attracted to the flowers which also have medicinal properties. The wood of these fast growing trees is light and widely used for making boats and for matches. This and "Sal" are fire-climax trees in the Tarai.

c Map showing popular lowland areas of Nepal :\Lumbini, the birthplace of the Buddha and Chitwan National Park which still has rhinos, tigers and other wild animals.

103a Although often hot and dusty, the Terai can be very interesting and colorful as either fertile farmland or tropical forests. Sugarcane, jute and rice have often taken the place of the great forests as malaria has been eliminated. Not all of the soil is fertile, however, since rocks and gravel cover much of the plains nearest the Churia Hills and streams go underground.

b Belfruit tree and great chautara tree outlined against sunset at Lumbini.

104 "Bhendi" (*Thespesia populnea*) is a pretty member of the
a & b Mallow family which grows as a subropical scrub on steep slopes of deep gorges.

105 Variety in Subrtopical Leguminosae.

a & b "Phaledo" (*Erythrina stricta*) is a small tree of 15–20 ft. which produces bright red flowers on leafless branches just after the "Simal" has finished blooming in the spring. Swarms of birds and butterflies then visit these flowers for their nectar.

c The Himalayan Coral Bean (*Erythrina arborescence*) blooms in the autumn. It grows to a height of as much as 10 ft. and is generally found in wet subtropical valleys. These were in western Bhutan.

d *Butea minor* usually occurs along gorges and bears very large leaves with 3 leaflets. The seeds are used in traditional medicine to repel round worms from children.

e "Palas" (*Butea frondosa*) is generally known as the "Flame of the forest" due to its bright colored flowers that appear profusely on the tree. This is a sub-tropical species which usually occurs in Terai forests.

106a More variety in subtropical Leguminosae–
Mimosa rubicaulis grows along rivers and trails as a 3 to 8 ft shrub. It is related to the small Sensitive Plant which drops and folds its leaves upon being touched. Neither is very common in Nepal. This thorny shrub was growing at Trisuli.

b *Caesalpinia pulcherrima* This is a small veriety of Gul Mohur which was introduced many years ago to India and has spread wherever there have been British Gurkha army camps. This small tree was growing in Pokhara.

107a *Bauhinia variegata,* the "Koiralo" is often seen as a village shrub but it can be quite abundant on steep slopes of sub-tropical valleys. Fresh flowers and buds are edible as a vegetable and dried ones are stored as a medicine for the cure of dysentery, diarrhoea and other types of stomach disorders.
Euphorbia royleana (center foreground) is a common "cactus" of tropical and subropical valleys. The latex is generally used as a fish poison. The latex of this plant and rocks on which it grows combine together to produce the famous "Silajet" of Ayurvedic medicine.

b *Albizia mollis* "Siris" occurs mostly along humid valleys of subtropical Nepal. This was flowering in upper Bheri (W. Nepal) in late May.

108a (*Shorea robusta*) Sal leaves are very popular for making traditional plates, "lapes" & "tapari" for picnics and feasts. Winged sal seeds shown on leaf yield a fixed oil.

b In spring the old leaves of the Sal turn red and drop off as yellow flowers and new green leaves appear. These straight trees have been cut rather close to their trunks because of the demand for leaves. The river is red as it carries red mud from freshly plowed fields.

109a Preparation of Sal plates is exclusively handled by ladies and a scene of sewing sal leaves into plates with bamboo needles is an indication of some ceremony or festival.

b Sal trees are common in the Terai, and in lowland valleys below 2,500 ft. These are Nepal's most valuable timber tree and once formed a continuous forest along the foothills of the western Himalayas almost to Sikkim, where Teak (*Tectona grandis*) has been planted. The Sal forests of Nepal are regarded as an extension of the Dipterocarpus forests of S. E. Asia but they are rather light and open as compared to those of the latter. These forests are vanishing rapidly from the Nepal Terai following human migration from the hills in malaria-free regions.

c & d *Lobelia pyramidalis* "Eklebir" is a tall plant of 2 to 8 ft. often growing in open patches in temperate forests. This was seen along the road between Kathmandu and Pokhara. The stems and leaves have medicinal properties.

110 Evening scenes along the Rapti River from "Tiger Tops Lodge". There are now a number of tourist lodges near Chitwan National Park where one can enjoy tropical vegetation and jungle animals from the back of an elephant or an easy chair on the lawn. Tiger Tops was the first.

a *Dillenia pentagyne* "Tantari" is an associate of the Terai Sal forest. It has very large leaves and occurs as a second layer tree.

b Numerous species of Bauhina occur in Nepal. In Terai Sal forests Bauhina is quite common as a climber. Leaves of *Bauhinia* are useful for thatching roofs, for making traditional water proofs "ghum" and also are used as a cigarette wrapper for local cigarettes "Bidi".

c Riverine vegetàtion of *Acacia* and *Dalbergia* (Khair-Sisso) mixed with tall elephant grasses and Sal forest make a perfect habitat for deer, rhinos, tigers and other tropical animals. Crocodiles, dolphins and ducks may be seen in the river.

111a Early morning dew sparkles on the web of a small grass spider in the grounds of Tiger Tops. Those who merely wander near the lodges of the various camps in Chitwan

National Park can also find beauty in small animal life.

b This garden spider has completely wrapped its prey in cords of its own making. Since the prey is often grasshoppers and similar insects that enjoy eating the vegetation, the spider is a friend of the plants.

c A small liazard surveys the scene from the top of an acanthaceae plant. The marking on the flower bracts resembles the scales of the lizard. As an enthusiastic eater of insects, the lizard helps the plants when those eaten are injurious to the plant.

112a & b Hill people are moving to the lowlands. For many years a night spent in the Terai lowlands or Churia Hills in the rainy season was almost a death sentence. Malaria protected the tropical forests and wild animals by killing all but the most hardy settlers. Today, with malaria eradication programs, people have found a new fertile area to clear and settle. Hill people were encouraged to move here and clear the forests rather than clear and terrace more land in the hills where erosion soon removes the soil and fertility. The settlers in the Chitwan valley are mostly Gurung, Magar and Chhetri.

The ferry boats are made of Simal trunks. Many of the people using the ferry are porters carrying merchandise from the larger settlements near the Indian border to hill villages. New settlers also keep in contact with their relatives in the hills.

113a "Bihaya" (*Ipomoea fistulosa*) is a common wayside hedge shrub of the Terai region. It is easily propagated by cuttings. This plant is said to be posionous to goats.

b A tiny, often brightly colored duckweed covers the flooded fields and rice paddies in the spring. (*Azolla imbricata*)

c The Railway Creeper (*Ipomoea palmata*) Since this vine can be grown from cuttings, it is an easy plant to grow in the Terai to cover walls.

d *Porana grandiflora* is seen in the temperate broad-leaved forest as a conspicuous climber. It is one of the many members of the Morning glory Family to be called "Bindweed".

ROADSIDE PLANTS

114a *Hypericum* or "St. John's Wort" is commonly seen on open dry slopes and along forest edges among shrubs. It is a perennial shrub and sometimes covers big patches on the slope – as seen along the Raj Path as it leaves the Kathmandu Valley. Its flowering indicates the advent of spring in hilly regions. There are some 7 species in Nepal.

b *Reinwardtia trigyna* or "Pyauli" is one of the few plants flowering in late autumn and winter. It is a woody member of the Flax or Linaceae Family and the plant size varies from a few inches to 5–8 ft. depending upon the availability of moisture in the soil.

c *Calotropis gigantea* – "Aak" is a giant milkweed plant of the Terai and wastelands. It has many medicinal uses.

d *Rhus succedanea* – "Rani Bhalayo" The Sumac produces very colorful leaves in winter. Its milky sap causes allergic blisters.

114e *Colquhounia coccinea* occurs along forest edges and clearings. It is a conspicuous shrub with bright flowers often seen at 8,000–9,000 ft. altitude. This one was blooming near Paro, Bhutan in late August.

f *Woodfordia fruticosa* – "Dhainyaro" has nectar which is enjoyed by children and small birds. It often grows on the cliff sides of river terraces along with pink *Luculia* and yellow *Reinwardtia,* though it blooms in the spring and the others bloom in fall and winter respectively. It also occurs near the edges of Chir pine forest as an undershrub. The dried flowers have a medicinal value and are used in disorders of mucus membrane especially during dysentery.

115a The Woolly Mint (*Colebrookea oppositifolia*) usually comes up as a secondary growth of shrubs in cleared forests on dry situations. Flowering spikes look quite unusual for its family. (Labiatae)

The *Hamiltonia suaveolens* behind does not cover large areas and is generally seen growing sparcely among other shrubs. (Rubiaceae)

b The bright blue Indian Acanthus (*Acanthaceae*) shrub grows best in wet places along forest edges. This one was seen near Tiger Tops in March. Most people familiar with Greek architecture are more familiar with the large deeply cut leaves of the European Acanthus used to decorate the Corinthian columns on temples.

c The Paper chase (*Mussaenda macrophylla*) locally known as "Dhobini" or little washerwoman is a member of Rubiaceae which stands out in the forest because of its showy leaf bract. The advent of the Monsoon is generally followed by the flowering of *Mussaenda* in Subtropical Nepal and Bhutan.

d *Bauhinia* vines are characteristic of the dry Terai forest. The woody vines clasp tall Sal trees. The leaf often resembles the almost heart shaped footprint of the camel so they have been called "Camel's foot".

116 Favorite treks north of Kathmandu are to Langtang, Gosainkund, and to Helembu. One can see glaciers, lakes or a little Himalayan version of Switzerland.

117a The hills around the valley of Kathmandu have forest with Oaks unless they are recolonized by Pines following clearings.

b The top of Sheopuri north of Kathmandu is a nice place to see Rhododendrons bloom in April. The *R. arboreum* may be seen in all color variations from scarlet to white.

c Hemlock – Rhododendron at about 10,000 ft. is one of the most spectacular forests in Nepal. Himalayan Hemlock, *Tsuga dumosa* is a magnificent tree of 80 ft. or more in height characteristic of humid regions in the Himalayas.

118a Flowers of *Polygonum* color the deforested slope along the trail to Gosainkund in August.

b The Sacred lake of Gosainkunda at 14,000 ft. attracts many pilgrims. Such pilgrims used to collect plants for Hamilton during his stay in Nepal (1802–3). Many new species were discovered in this way. *Juniperus recurva* is one of such plants. (see p. 155 p.)

119a To approach the Gosainkunda lakes from the Sundarijal trail a 15,000 ft. pass must be crossed and the lakes are first seen from above. Temporary shelters are set up for the pilgrims at the time of the full moon in August at the far side of this lake. On the return many go by way of Trisuli Bazar.

b Devout Hindus bathe in the icy waters as they worship Shiva. Buddhist Tamangs also worshiphere at the same time.

120a There are many types of *Impatiens* or Touch-me-nots to be found in the Himalayas. The Balsam Family ususlly grows in damp ravines and blooms during the summer monsoon. This waterfall along the trail to Gosainkund is a perfect setting for them.

b Yellow Balsam – one of the more than 25 species of *Impatiens* known to occur in Nepal. Their delicate flowers and watery stems require dampness and deep shade.

c Front and side views of a lavender Balsam to show flower structure.

121a White Balsam from the Gosainkunda area.

b Pink Balsam showing the impatient seed pods. When the seeds are ripe one need barely touch the pod and it will burst open and throw out the seeds with a little coiled spring device. This is the reason for the generic name "Impatients".

122a *Cyananthus lobatus*, from Bhutan.

b *Halenia elliptica* looks like a tiny Columbine but it is a member of the Gentain Family. It can be found in the upper Temperate Region (between 8,000 and 10,000 ft.) It susually is on the forest floor but this was blooming in an open field near Paro, Bhutan.

122c *Meconopsis paniculata* The mountain poppies of the Himalayas have rossettes of leaves in the winter and early spring. Soft hairs on the leaves are often characteristic of high altitude plants which may otherwise suffer severe evaporation loss.

d Most poppies bloom during the monsoon. These lovely yellow poppies with their delicate petals can be seen above 12,000 ft. in the month of August.

e *Cyananthus lobatus* is a sub-alpine flower which can be found around 11,000 ft. in open meadows. They were found in good numbers both near Gosainkiund and on the pass between Paro and Thimpu in Bhutan.

f *Aquilegia vulgaris* "Columbine" as seen near Pisang in Manang Valley.

123a *Cornus capitata* This Dogwood grows as a small tree in subtropical gorges and humid habitats. This was near Gasa on the Kali Gandaki. Showy bracts look like petals. The fruits are sweet and eaten by local inhabitants.

b The buttercups are represented by more than 15 species and generally occur in small colonies. They prefer wet and marshy areas or open meadows.

c *Meconopsis simplicifolia* is one of the pretty blue poppies of the Himalayas. It occurs among boulders in the alpine and subalpine region. This one was blooming in June on the Namum Pass at over 12,000 ft.

d *Saxifraga diversifolia* occurs among rocks and in shady localities in temperate forests at around 10,000 ft. altitude.

e *Potentilla fulgens* "Cinquefoil" is a common hill plant on exposed grassy slopes between 4,000 and 7,000 ft.

f The Potentilla is seen with *Agrimonia*, another member of the Rose Family.

124a *Didymocarpus* sp. "Kumkum Dhup" generally grows on limestone rocks in humid temperate forests. This plant is used for making incense.

b Another species of *Didymocarpus* on mossy rocks.

c White Anemone and pink ground orchid are seen together in sub-alpine meadows.

d Yellow Violets and the pink *Roscoa* grow in the deep shade in temperate forests. at 9,000 ft.

e *Pedicularis* sp. and a tiny pink orchid with seemingly similar flowers grow together in the Trisuli Valley.

f *Pedicularis megalantha* grows in profusion near the monasterry belowGosainkund. They are best seen in forest clearings.

125a *Begonia picta* "Magar kanche" is pictured against a rock. The wild Begonia can be found on wet slopes in deep shade. Many cultivated varieties have been developed from the various wild forms found in the Himalayas.

b *Martynia diandra* has lovely flowers with sticky glandular hairs. This large leaved plant grows as a weed in waste lands of the subtropical valleys between 2,000 and 3,000 ft. It may attain a height of 3 ft.

126a Some bright weeds from the wheat fields. Throughout the world we find attractive weeds mixed with the cultivated crops and many of these weeds are almost as universal as the crops. Here in the temperate region of Rara Lake we find Pinks, Shephered's Purse and red Poppies. (*Papaver dubium.*)

b The yellow *Dicentra scandens* is a climbing member of the Fumitory Family. People from America can see its similarity to Golden Smoke and Dutchmen's Britches of the same family. The Barleria below is a wayside shrub. They were growing near Goropani along the trail to Jomsom. Since the *Dicentra* was in heavy shade it was placed on a lichen covered rock for the photograph.

c The Mexican Poppy, *Argemone mexicana*, is a weedy shrub growing in subrtopical wastelands. Its seeds yields an oil which is dangerous to eat. Mustard oil has been known to be adulterated with this oil with disasterous results when used for cooking.

d *Strobilanthus* is another wayside flower found in the temperate forest regions. This was also growing along the trail to Ghoropani.

127a *Hippophae salicifolia* grows as a shrub of 6 to 10 ft. along rivers of the inner valleys. This plant also has a dwarf form of only a few inches tall. Here it is seen in the upper Kali Gandaki.

b *Incarvillae arguta* is a characteristic plant along the gorges of big rivers. It often is seen as a rich spray of flowers on overhanging rocks.

c *Hippophae salicifolia* detail. This was growing in the lower Langtang Valley

128 The Mushrooms of the Himalayas are not yet investigated systematically and certainly warrents the interest of Botanists.

a Malamche is an almost Swiss type village which can be reached in a short 2 or 3 day trek from Kathmandu.

b *Marasminum*

c *Amanita* sp. This species looks very much like the deadly "Death Angel" and "Fly Agaric" and is doubtless also poisonous.

d *Cantharellus* sp.

e *Russula* sp. The *Russula emetica* which this resembles is emetic as its name indicates. It is lovely to look at, however.

129a *Amanita* sp. This large delicate mushroom was growing in Bhutan.

b *Boletus* sp. The *Boletus* mushrooms have pores instead of gills. This one was on the trail between Paro and Thimpu, Bhutan.

c Mushrooms may not be well investigated by the botanist but local people have discovered which are safe to eat and sell them locally.

d Scarlet Cup mushrooms (*Aleuria aurantiaca*) are known in many parts of the world. Here it is shown with Ardisia berries.

e Red Polypores growing on dead wood in Arun Valley. Chilauni flowers have fallen from the tree above.

f Here is a rather sticky mushroom growing near the *Boletus* in Bhutan.

130 MORE HIMALAYAN MUSHROOMS

a *Dacromyces plamata* on lichen covered log.

b *Amanita* sp. This mushroom seems to be the same species

as that on the previous page (129 a) This was so large that it broke when we attempted to pick it. A friend in Bhutan said that it was eaten there but I am not sure how the Sherpas feel about it in Solu where this was growing. In the west the *Amanita* Mushrooms are usually avoided because of the very dangerous species in this family.

c The woody Polypores keep very well for display purposes but no one cares about eating such leathery or woody mushrooms.

d *Schizophyllum* sp. from Arun Valley.

e *Russula* species are very attractive. Here is a gray type with red-capped emetica types. It is not known whether the yellow stem of the small one will turn white with age. These were found along the trail to Gosainkunda.

f A slightly different type of *Boletus* from western Bhutan. These rapidly turned blue when broken or pressed.

131 Morels (*Morchella esculenta*) growing with Jack-in-the-pulpit (*Arisaema nepanthoides*). These were seen in the Rhododendron woods between Ghandrung and Ghoropani at about 9,500 ft. in June.

132 The E verest or Solu Khumbu Area is one of the most beautiful regions in the world. The setting for the world's highest mountain is well worth seeing whether one is a climber or nature lover. The Buddhist Monasterry at Thangboche is seen here in two moods with its mountain setting.

133 From above the Thangboche Monasterry one can look back at the mountains surrounding Namche Bazar and Khumjung and Kunde in the valley above. The small sketch map shows the location of major trails and air strips.

134 Autumn months are generally clear and cold as November comes on. At the higher elevations on the way to Everest Base Camp the vegetation is sparce and already dry in most cases. This alpine meadow at 17,000ft. near Khumbhu glacier would have been green during the summer.

b The only mushrooms here are rocks with ice stems. The rock has shaded the ice and kept it from melting.

135 At 18,000 ft. above the Base Camp we found lichens and Edelweiss. High altitude plants, like many desert plants must withstand winds which cause evaporation. Tiny leaves with soft fuzz are likely to be found.

b *Lagotis glauca*, and other dried plants still look almost alive in the dried lakebed of Gorakshep at almost 18,000 ft.

136a *Ephedra gerardiana* grows among rocks at drier places in the Inner Valleys at around 14,000 ft. The plants have medicinal properties and is the source of the alkaloid ephedrine.

b Closeup of plant in Everest area.

137 Edelweiss *Leontopodium* species are quite abundant at higher elevations (15,000 to 18,000 ft. or higher) A thorough study on Himalayan Edelweiss would prove quite rewarding. Switzerland has made a good thing of this flower.

138a High altitude Gentian species around rocks and open meadows are one of the few flowers to be seen during autumn.

b Detail of Gentian flower

c Spring and summer Plants are already dried out in September but the leaves of a drying Primrose are still colorful in November.

139a *Piptanthus nepalensis,* the Himalayan Laburnum is a shrub that grows around 11,000 and 12,000 ft. Just below timberline.

b Another high altitude member or the Pea Family is this strange Black Pea, *Thermopsis barbata.* It was seen in June behind both Dhaulagiri and Annapurna at around 12,000 ft.

c The Elderberry *Sambucus adnata* and related species are seen from the lower valleys to 9,000 ft. in moist locations.

d There are many kinds of Sage in the Himalayas and they have many local uses-from rubbing on the skin to discourage leeches to placing in beds to get rid of fleas. Sherpas use this sage to sweep floors and make things smell fresh.

140 *Lilium nepalense,* "Ban lasun" occurs among grasses and ferns at about 7,000 to 8,000 ft. It flowers during the summer and monsoon months. The bulbs are used as medicine and are also used as poison carried in the 'darts' used for poaching musk-deer in western Nepal.

141 The Easter Lily type *Lilium wallichiana* occurs in subtropical valleys among grasses and bushes. It is a rare plant that flowers during the autumn season.

142a This conifierous forest consists of *Pinus wallichiana* and could well be the secondary forest. Original forest at this 8,000 ft. altitude in east Nepal should generally contain

Rhododendrons and oaks.

b The Hemlock (*Tsuga dumosa*) forms a dense forest with an undergrowth of Rhododendrons and Maples. Hemlock forests are found only in the humid temperate regions on the south of the main Himalayan range.

c Although Hemlock trees are gigantic, their cones are very small, smaller than a pigeon's egg.

143 The upper Temperate forests in east Nepal have a number of deciduous trees. *Magnolia campbellii,* with its profusion of flowers is most conspicuous. This tree is characteristic of the eastern Himalaya and does not occur in the western half of Nepal and beyond.

144 Sketch map of far eastern Nepal to western Bhutan.

145a Dhankuta, with its white-washed houses and flowers on the balconies is typical of the hill villages in eastern Nepal.

b Two more friends of the plants found in sub-tropical forests and forest clearings. The Blue throated Barbet was raised from a small nestling and became an enthusiastic hunter of fairly large insects before flying to freedom in the tall trees.

c The Praying Mantis waits for insects to come close and grabs them with its front legs.

146 A two or three hours walk up through lichen covered ever-green forest will bring one to a group of Buddhist Monas-terries placed precariously on the rocky cliffs at around 10,000 ft. The trail is pleasant and many flowers can be seen along the way.

147 Many species of *Geranium* are found in the Himalayas.
a In Nepal alone there are 15 species which grow from the
& sub-tropical to the sub-alpine zone. These two types of wild
b geraniums were both growing along the trail in Bhutan.

c This delicate little climber grew by the bridge just before Tiger's Nest. We were not able to identify it but reluctent to leave it out because of the lack of a name. It seems to fall somewhere between the Gentian vines and the Blue bells. of Campanulaceae.

d The Pomegranate is Mediterranian in origin. It is one of the Mediterranian type plants growing wild in the dry valley behind Dhaulagiri near Tibrikot. They were also growing in what may have been second growth jungle near Punaka, Bhutan. In this location they might have been cul-tivated plants gone wild.

149a This white Ginger, *Costus specious* is an especially attractive member of *Gingiberaceae.* The plant grows to 5 or 6 ft. and flowers during the monsoon period. It grows in subtropical ravines and may be cultivated for its rhizomes which yield diasgenin, a steroid of medicinal use.

b The *Curcuma augustifolia* seem to have pink flowers. Actually the flowers are small yellow trumpets hidden by the large showy pink bracts. The flowering stalk precedes the large leaves which later grow very tall and dense wherever these plants have gotten a foothold. They are generally found in the midland hills between 3,000 and 6,000 ft. in open places.

c *Hedychium ellipticum* "Kamuna" has fragrant flowers and is quite popular among the inhabitants of Kathmandu as an item to offer the Living Goddess, Kumari during Indra Jatra in late August or early September.

148c The Crepe Myrtle (*Lagerstroemia indica*) has very distinctive flowers which come in many colors from white to pink and lavender. It has been planted widely in Kathmandu Valley and grows as either a bush or tree. Since it flowers during the month of Ashad (June-July) and so is known locally as "Ashare Phul."

a&b Forest tree of the same family but with smaller white flowers was photographed from the Arun Valley region in June. This tree may attain a large size in the Bhabhar forest along the Himalayan foothills. (*Lagerstroemia parviflora*)

d "Lampati" (*Duabanga grandiflora*) was also growing in the lower Arun Valley forest and blooming in June. It is a tall straight tree of about 40 ft. Generally limited to tropical regions of east Nepal below 2,500 ft.

151 Our local Arun Valley "Sherpa" expresses his cheerful mood with bright berries of *Clerodendron infortunatum* with their red persisting sepals. Below is a detail of the spray. *Clerodendron infortunatum* is one of the commonest shrubs in the Sal forests of subtropical valleys and the Terai region.

150a *Holarrhena antidysenterica,* "Indra jau" is another associate of the Sal forest below 2,500 ft. altitude. The tree is generally small (10 to 20 ft.) and flowers in early June. It has certain medicinal properties such as for the cure of dysentry and other stomach disorders.

150b The Screw Pine *Pandanus furcatus* occurs in the malarial marsh or the Terai and Duars of the eastern Himalaya. It

often attains a height of 10 – 20 ft. and may be quite conspicuous in eastern Nepal.
The fruiting of *Pandanus* is very pretty and resembles the pineapple. The white Jasmine flowers around it help to emphasize the red color of the fruit.

152a Alder woods play a very important role in the soil conservation of hilly regions. Slopes devastated by landslides can hardly support any trees except the Alder (*Alnus nepalensis*) or "Utis". The presence of alder woods is a sure indication of humid soil and so suitable location for Cardamon cultivation.

b Waxy pink flowers of *Ardisia solanacea.*

c *Engenia jambos,* the "Jamun" tree is in the same family as the Eucalyptus. It flowers in late spring and produces a greenish sweet fruit during late summer which is sold on the market. The "Jamun" tree is not seen in forests but are often planted as garden trees. This was in Pokhara Valley.

d Humid regions are readily indicated by the presence of a rich epiphytic flora. As such, the *Aeschynanthus parviflorus* with its leathery leaves and bunch of pendulous fruits hang down from branches of tall trees. Its flowers are very brightly coloured orange-red.

e Cypress trees are, on the other hand, found mostly in drier regions with hardly any epiphytes. The tree occurs in the limestone country of western and central Nepal. It has a columnar crown and attains a height of 60 ft.

153 Natural vegetation alone has been used in the construction of this suspension bridge over the Arun river at Num. It was recommended that only local porters be hired since they knew the bridge and would not be afraid to cross. It was only safe for one or two at a time and the engineer waiting for supplies for a modern bridge did not expect this to last out the season. Usually such bridges have a very short life.

155a Fir forests occur just above the belt of human habitation on the south of the main Himalayan range. Undisturbed naural forests are, therefore, to be seen above 9,000 ft. Fir forests give way to bushy rhododendrons and birch trees near the timberline above 12,000 ft.

b Female cones of the Fir, *Abies spectabilis* stand erect on branchlets covered with linear leaves. These cones yield a blue-black hue which is used as a dye.

c Himalayan Hemlock *Tsuga dumosa* are magnificent trees of 60 – 80 ft. which often grow on north facing slopes with a second story of maples and Rhododendrons. These were on the pass between Thimpu and Punaka in Bhutan.

154a Himalayan Larch, *Larix griffithii* has hanging branchlets with small upright cones. It is endemic to eastern Himalaya (E. Nepal, Sikkim and Bhutan) It grows with firs and rhododendrons above 10,000 ft. to 12,000 ft.

b *Juniperus recurva* often grows to a tree of 20 or 30 ft. and the wood and twigs are used as an incense "Dhup" throughout the Himalayan region. The scent is used in most of the religious rites performed by Sherpas and Tibetans. Balls of paste from the wood are sold on the market.

c The Larch of Langtang corresponds to the Szechwan Larch *Larix potanini*. It is an unique species of Lantang and deserves special protection. Unlike other coniferous trees, the larch trees shed their leaves in winter.

156a Eastern Himalaya (E. Nepal, Sikkim and Bhutan) is the home of Rhododendrons. During the period from March to May a procession of different species come into flower beginning with the red tree form at 4,500 ft. The miriads of color of temperate and sub-alpine species is best seen in May. Rhododendron blooms stand out against fir trees in the fog.

b New leaves on many species of *Rhododendron* have specially colored bracts that fail off soon after the leaves unfold to their size.

c Milke Danda, the long mountain barrier that divides the Arun Valley and the Tamur Valley in East Nepal is perhaps the most beautiful ridge to trek on during April and May. One could start at Dhankuta and may continue north to Topke Gola counting colors on various species of Rhododendron from 8,000 ft. to 13,000 ft. or even more. One may encounter well over two dozen species.

157a This collection shows *Rhododendron hodgsonii* with a dense cluster of rich pink flowers on the left and on the top of the picture. It is followed by a spray of red *Rh. arboreum*. The slender bells with orange, red or yellowinsh colors are the flowers of *Rh. cinnabarinum* while the pinkish white and mauve flowers belong to *Rh. campanulatum*. The loose spray of creamy flowers are *Rh. campylocarpum*.

b Sheep have kept the grass down and avoided the Rhododendrons making a park,-like setting for the Rhododendron display.

159a *Rhododendron campanulatum* flowers come in different shades of pink and mauve. It is almost always present in the shrubland that marks the upper limit of tree vegetation at about 13,000 ft. The velvety felt underneath the leaves is unique to this species.
The wooden handle of the "Khukuri" knife is seen sticking out from the belt of the mountain man.

b *Rhododendron arboreum* has dense clusters of flowers on branchlets. This high altitude form has rusty brown tomentum underneath the leaves while those at lower altitudes are silvery beneath the leaves.

c Attractive lily-of-the-valley type flowers of *Pieris formosa* adorn this relative of the Rhododendrons found between 8,000 and 9,000 ft. This and the similar *Lyonia ovalifolia* are both called "Angeri" locally and their young leaves are especially poisonous to animals. The latter grows from 5,000 to 8,000 ft.

158a *Rhododendron thomsonii* generally occur as a shrub of 15–20 ft. with twisted and gnarled trunks at about 11,000 – 12,000 ft. The red calyx on the deep red flowers is characteristic.

b Red, white, and orange flowers of Rhododendron all occur together between 11,000 and 12,000 ft. during May in eastern Nepal.

c *Rhododendron hodgsonii* is one of the attractive forms at about 12,000 ft. This is where we are first able to find the yellow bells of *Rh. campylocarpum*.

160a *Rhododendron campylocarpum* growing as a sub-alpine bush of 6 to 10 ft. on Milke Danda in May.

b *Rhododendron cinnabarinum* comes in different shades of yellow and orange color. It is also a plant of sub-alpine shrubery.

c *Rhododendron campanulatum* has bell-shaped flowers and occurs all along the Himalayas from Kashmir to Bhutan (see p. 158 a)

d *Rhododendron lepidotum* "Bhale Sunpate" is a small shrub of 1 ft. to 4 ft. often forming loose clumps. Two color forms are generally met with. It occurs all along the Himalayas from 10,000 to 15,000 ft.

161a Most of the tropical orchids are epiphytic. This lavender orchid is on a mossy tree tunk in subtropical vegetation.

b Pink lady's slipper *Cypripidium macranthum* is a high altitude ground orchid at 11,000 ft. This is an east Himalayan plant. Here it was growing in the Marsyangdi valley way west from its normal area of geographical distribution.

c Ground orchids are not so showy as the epiphytic ones. The green ground orchid *Habenaria* and the pink *Satyrium* are pictured together. They occur almost together on open grassy slopes at about 10,000 ft. altitude.

d The pink *Satyrium* is growing together with the everlasting *Anaphalis*.

162a *Coelogyne* species are well known for their white flowers and Nepalese call them "Chandi gava" or silver orchid. This *Coelogyne ochracea* was growing on a tree in the sub-tropical Arun Valley. It was blooming in May.

b *Coelogyne cristata* occurs on rocks in humid moist regions such as Pokhara. They start to bloom when the weather starts getting hot in April.

163. *Coelogyne cristata* grows both on rocks and on tree trunks. It often has a series of pseudobulbs on a running stem. This plant is common in humid regions between 3,000 and 6,000 ft.

164 a&b *Dendrobium nobile* shown in detail and as a spray growing below was blooming in the lower part of Arun Valley in May. They generally grow on tall tree branches in the humid valleys of eastern Himalayas below 4,000 ft.

c *Pleione hookeriana* is a shade loving orchid of dense oak forests at 8,000–9,000 ft. It grows on mossy tree trunks.

165a The humid climate of the Pokhara region to the south of Machhapuchhare is readily indicated by its rich epiphytic flora. Here a golden *Dendrobium* is growing with the *Aeschynanthus*, both epiphytic on a Chilaune tree.

b *Calanthe tricarinata* is a ground orchid of the temperate oak forest at about 8,000 ft. It grows in the shade of the trees.

166a Temperate Himalaya has a large number of ferns both terrestrial and epiphytic. Some tropical species penetrate into Nepal from S. E. Asia through Assam.
The *Thelypteris* sp. are commonly found along ravines and gullies between 5,000 and 6,000 ft. This was on the hills above Pokhara.

b *Nephrolepis cordifolia* "Panisaro" has underground watery tubers and grows among rocks and boulders on dry situations. The tubers are eaten by thirsty travellers.

c *Drynaria* sp. "Nest fern" grows on tree trunks and are quite common in sub-tropical regions.

d *Cythea spinulosa* "Tree Fern" is a member of the tropical monsoon forest. It is quite common along east Himalayas. The tree fern is about 15 ft. tall.

167a *Dicranopteris linearis* is common on dry slopes with deforested vegetation at about 5,000 – 6,000 ft.

167b *Woodwardia unigemmata* is another dry place fern. It is seen here with a small blue butterfly.

168 Forest clearings get luxuriant vegetation during the monsoon. Here we see the orchid-like *Roscoea purpurea* with its bright purple flowers above Helembu in August. "Rasgari" is a member of the Ginger Family.

169a The Jack-fruit, *Artocarpus integrifolia* has huge fruits weighing several kilogıams and they are borne directly on tree trunks and branches. The fruit has a delicious fruity flesh. The seeds are also roasted and eaten. The Jack-fruit occurs in subtropical valleys below 3,000 tt.

b The banana *Musa paradiciaca* is cultivated in all the tropical and subtropical regions of the world. In the Himalayas, the deep river valleys and terai region have banana in cultivation. The native wild banana in the Himalaya does not have good enough fruits to bring it into cultivtion.

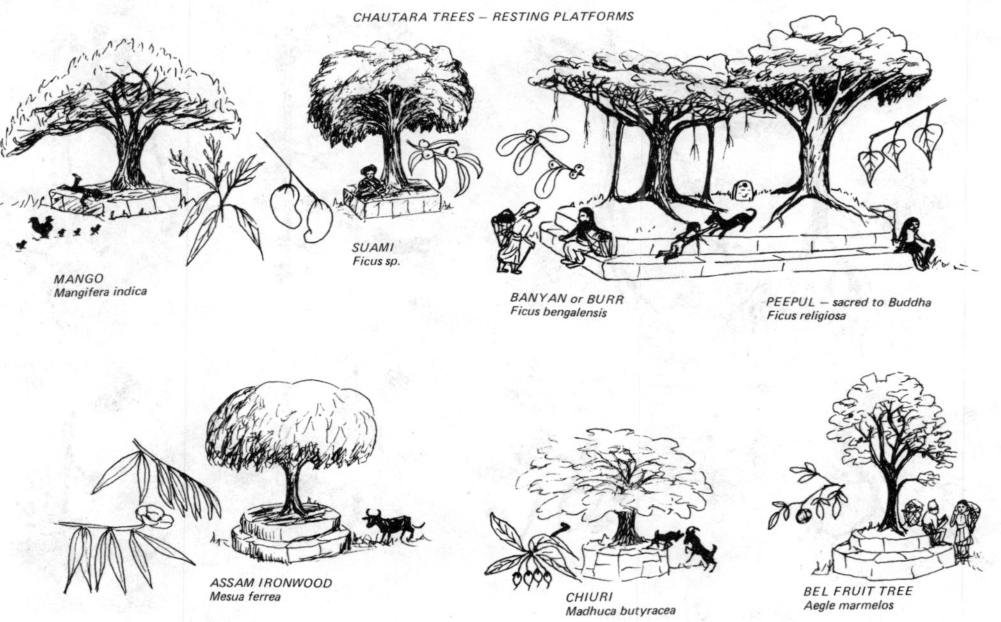
CHAUTARA TREES – RESTING PLATFORMS
MANGO
Mangifera indica
SUAMI
Ficus sp.
BANYAN or BURR
Ficus bengalensis
PEEPUL – sacred to Buddha
Ficus religiosa
ASSAM IRONWOOD
Mesua ferrea
CHIURI
Madhuca butyracea
BEL FRUIT TREE
Aegle marmelos

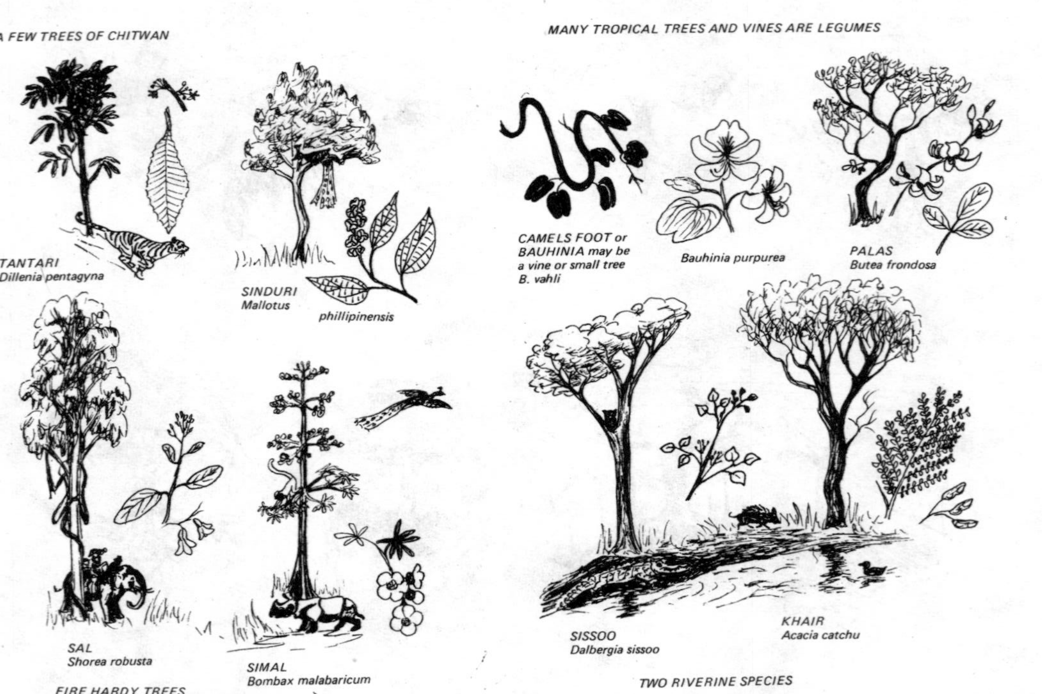
A FEW TREES OF CHITWAN
TANTARI
Dillenia pentagyna
SINDURI
Mallotus
phillipinensis
SAL
Shorea robusta
SIMAL
Bombax malabaricum
FIRE HARDY TREES
MANY TROPICAL TREES AND VINES ARE LEGUMES
CAMELS FOOT or
BAUHINIA may be
a vine or small tree
B. vahli
Bauhinia purpurea
PALAS
Butea frondosa
SISSOO
Dalbergia sissoo
KHAIR
Acacia catchu
TWO RIVERINE SPECIES

Index of pictures (plant names)

(A)

(C)

(D)

Publisher's Note

This little picture guide book should be useful to all who are interested in flowers whether students, tourists or nature lovers. Those who trek will find it easy to carry and divided into sections which correspond with the major treks of Nepal. Besides illustrating a large number of the trees and flowers likely to be seen in the Himalayas, this book also shows the diverse settings in which they are found and tells something about the inter-relationship of the plants with the local people.

The first part of the book is devoted to the important plant families and should help the beginner to identify plants. The second part consists of over 400 color pictures of flowers, trees, settings, people and little guide maps. The third part consists of notes and explanations of the plant pictures. A light reading through the notes should provide quite a bit of information about the natural history and ecology of Himalayan plants.

All the pictures were taken by Miss Dorothy Mierow between 1962 and 1978 during her years of living in Nepal when she made special excursions at different seasons to various localities in the Himalayas. Many more were taken than could be used here.

Botanical identification and subsequent explanations were done by Dr. Tirtha Bahadur Shrestha on the basis of his botanical collections and supported by other specimens of plants housed in the National Herbarium of Nepal and in the British Museum, London.

Miss Mierow, a graduate of Carleton College, has her M. S. degree in Biology from the U. of Pittsburgh and her M. A. in Geography from the U. of Minnesota. She taught both Biology and Geography before joining the Peace Corps and coming to Nepal in 1962. Since then she has spent about 11 years in Nepal teaching and working with the Natural History Museum of Prithvi Narayan Campus, Pokhara. She has made UNICEF maps on animals, birds, trees, flowers & butterflies, and a pictorial map of

Nepal. UNICEF published nine maps for the school children of Bhutan on similar natural history subjects after she had spent 2 months getting some firsthand information there. Recently her book "Wild Animals of Nepal" co-authored with Mr. Hemanta Mishra of the National Parks and Wildlife Dept. has come into the market. Miss Mierow is now associated with Prithvi Narayan Campus of Tribhuvan University. Her treks have covered most of the regions of Nepal as is evident from her photographs.

Dr. Shrestha is a Scientific Officer in the Dept. of Medicinal Plants, H.M.G. of Nepal and is in charge of the Botanical Survey and the Herbarium of Nepal. He has a M. Sc. in Botany from Muslim University, Aligarh, India and was specially trained in the British Museum (Natural History), London on the Systematic Botany. He recently got his Ph. D. from Grenoble University, France on his work on Ecology, Biogeography and Cartography of Northwest Nepal (Jumla and Saipal region). Dr. Shrestha has been associated with the Dept. of Medicinal Plants since 1960 and has made several botanical expeditions in the Nepal Himalayas.

Acknowledgements

The authors are thankful to all who have helped them during their course of separate treks and expeditions which are the basis of this book. Thanks are also due to Dr. Christian Kleinert who encouraged Miss. Mierow to take long treks.

Special thanks go to those who helped in the process of identification of pictures, such as Mr. P. R. Shakya, Mr. N.P. Manandhar, Mrs. P. Pradhan and Mrs. V. L. Gurung. A debt of gratitude goes to Dr. S. B. Malla and Dr. S. B. Rajbhandari for allowing the use of the library and the herbarium of the Dept. of Medicinal Plants, H.M.G. of Nepal. The authors also wish to extend thanks to the keeper and the staff of the herbarium in the British Museum (Natural History) London for their courtesy and co-operation.

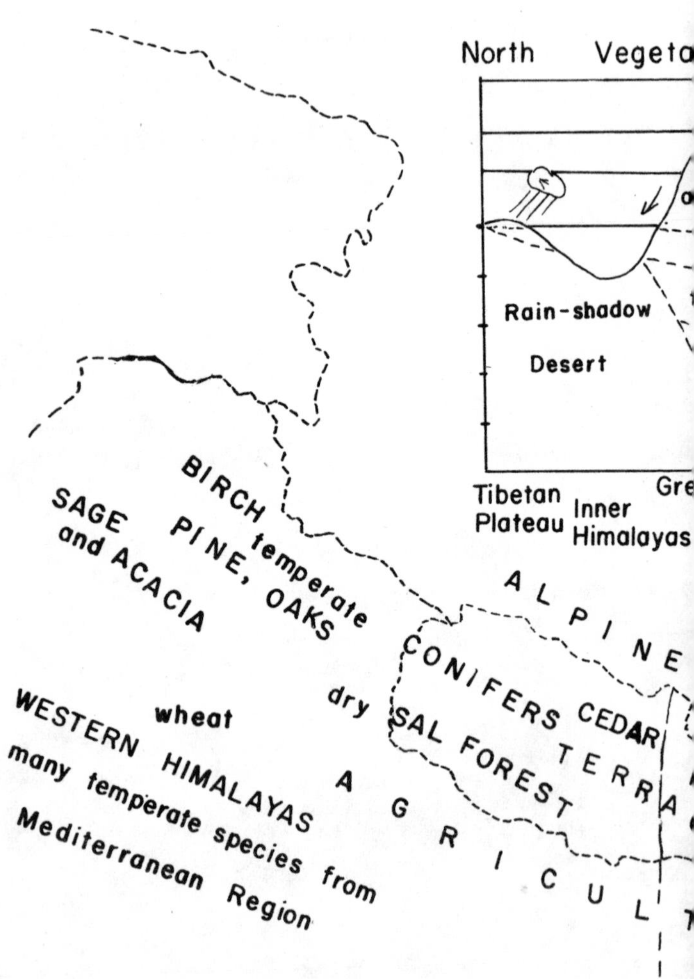
North
Rain-shadow
Desert
Tibetan Plateau
Inner Himalayas
BIRCH temperate
SAGE
PINE, OAKS
and ACACIA
ALPINE
CONIFERS CEDAR
dry
SAL FOREST
wheat
WESTERN HIMALAYAS
many temperate species from
Mediterranean Region

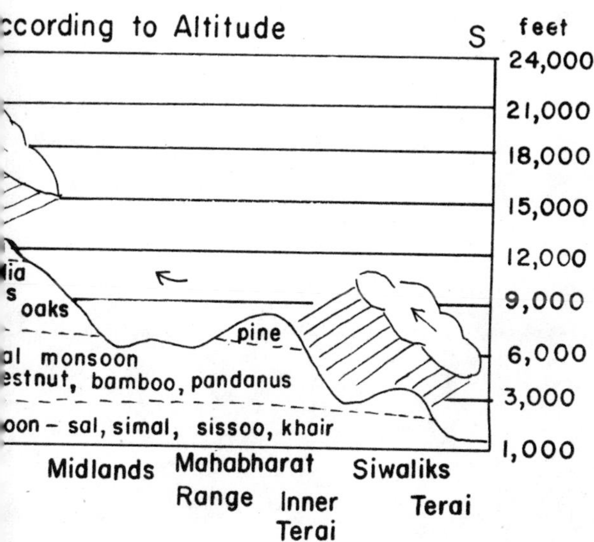
ccording to Altitude
S
feet
24,000
21,000
18,000
15,000
12,000
9,000
6,000
3,000
1,000
ia
s
oaks
pine
al monsoon
estnut, bamboo, pandanus
oon – sal, simal, sissoo, khair
Midlands
Mahabharat
Range
Inner
Terai
Siwaliks
Terai

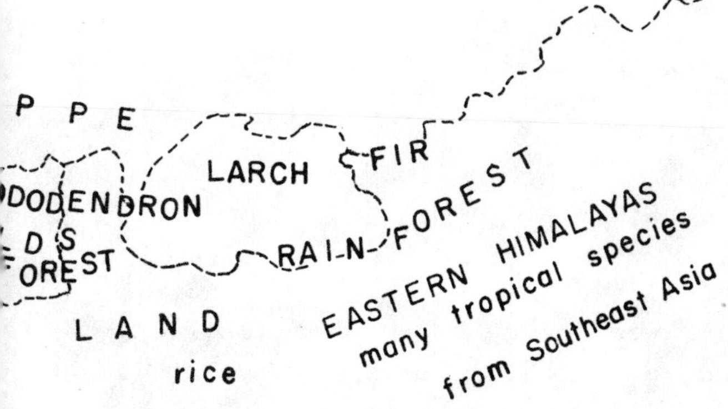
P P E
LARCH
FIR
DODENDRON
D S
OREST
RAIN FOREST
EASTERN HIMALAYAS
many tropical species
from Southeast Asia
L A N D
rice